GRADE 2

Curriculum Units

Measuring Length and Time

Measurement

UNIT 9

Complicated Kris Northern

"This image illustrates some of the best qualities of fractals—infinity, reiteration, and self similarity."– **Kris Northern**

Investigations
IN NUMBER, DATA, AND SPACE®

Measuring Length and Time

Measurement   UNIT 9

Glenview, Illinois • Boston, Massachusetts
Chandler, Arizona • Upper Saddle River, New Jersey

The Investigations curriculum was developed by TERC, Cambridge, MA.

This material is based on work supported by the National Science Foundation ("NSF") under Grant No. ESI-0095450. Any opinions, findings, and conclusions or recommendations expressed in this material are those of the author(s) and do not necessarily reflect the views of the National Science Foundation.

ISBN-13: 978-0-328-60019-9

ISBN-10: 0-328-60019-9

T E R C

Co-Principal Investigators

Susan Jo Russell

Karen Economopoulos

Authors

Lucy Wittenberg
Director Grades 3–5

Karen Economopoulos
Director Grades K–2

Virginia Bastable
(SummerMath for Teachers,
Mt. Holyoke College)

Katie Hickey Bloomfield

Keith Cochran

Darrell Earnest

Arusha Hollister

Nancy Horowitz

Erin Leidl

Megan Murray

Young Oh

Beth W. Perry

Susan Jo Russell

Deborah Schifter
(Education
Development Center)

Kathy Sillman

Administrative Staff

Amy Taber
Project Manager

Beth Bergeron

Lorraine Brooks

Emi Fujiwara

Contributing Authors

Denise Baumann

Jennifer DiBrienza

Hollee Freeman

Paula Hooper

Jan Mokros

Stephen Monk
(University of Washington)

Mary Beth O'Connor

Judy Storeygard

Cornelia Tierney

Elizabeth Van Cleef

Carol Wright

Technology

Jim Hammerman

Classroom Field Work

Amy Appell

Rachel E. Davis

Traci Higgins

Julia Thompson

Collaborating Teachers

This group of dedicated teachers carried out extensive field testing in their classrooms, met regularly to discuss issues of teaching and learning mathematics, provided feedback to staff, welcomed staff into their classrooms to document students' work, and contributed both suggestions and written material that has been incorporated into the curriculum.

Bethany Altchek

Linda Amaral

Kimberly Beauregard

Barbara Bernard

Nancy Buell

Rose Christiansen

Chris Colbath-Hess

Lisette Colon

Kim Cook

Frances Cooper

Kathleen Drew

Rebeka Eston Salemi

Thomas Fisher

Michael Flynn

Holly Ghazey

Susan Gillis

Danielle Harrington

Elaine Herzog

Francine Hiller

Kirsten Lee Howard

Liliana Klass

Leslie Kramer

Melissa Lee Andrichak

Kelley Lee Sadowski

Jennifer Levitan

Mary Lou LoVecchio

Kristen McEnaney

Maura McGrail

Kathe Millett

Florence Molyneaux

Amy Monkiewicz

Elizabeth Monopoli

Carol Murray

Robyn Musser

Christine Norrman

Deborah O'Brien

Timothy O'Connor

Anne Marie O'Reilly

Mark Paige

Margaret Riddle

Karen Schweitzer

Elisabeth Seyferth

Susan Smith

Debra Sorvillo

Shoshanah Starr

Janice Szymaszek

Karen Tobin

JoAnn Trauschke

Ana Vaisenstein

Yvonne Watson

Michelle Woods

Mary Wright

Note: Unless otherwise noted, all contributors listed above were staff of the Education Research Collaborative at TERC during their work on the curriculum. Other affiliations during the time of development are listed.

Advisors

Deborah Lowenberg Ball,
University of Michigan

Hyman Bass, Professor of Mathematics and Mathematics Education
University of Michigan

Mary Canner, Principal, Natick Public Schools

Thomas Carpenter, Professor of Curriculum and Instruction,
University of Wisconsin-Madison

Janis Freckmann, Elementary Mathematics Coordinator,
Milwaukee Public Schools

Lynne Godfrey, Mathematics Coach,
Cambridge Public Schools

Ginger Hanlon, Instructional Specialist in Mathematics,
New York City Public Schools

DeAnn Huinker, Director, Center for Mathematics and
Science Education Research, University of Wisconsin-Milwaukee

James Kaput, Professor of Mathematics, University of
Massachusetts-Dartmouth

Kate Kline, Associate Professor, Department of Mathematics
and Statistics, Western Michigan University

Jim Lewis, Professor of Mathematics,
University of Nebraska-Lincoln

William McCallum, Professor of Mathematics,
University of Arizona

Harriet Pollatsek, Professor of Mathematics,
Mount Holyoke College

Debra Shein-Gerson, Elementary Mathematics Specialist,
Weston Public Schools

Gary Shevell, Assistant Principal,
New York City Public Schools

Liz Sweeney, Elementary Math Department,
Boston Public Schools

Lucy West, Consultant, Metamorphosis:
Teaching Learning Communities, Inc.

This revision of the curriculum was built on the work of the many authors who contributed to the first edition (published between 1994 and 1998). We acknowledge the critical contributions of these authors in developing the content and pedagogy of *Investigations*:

Authors

Joan Akers

Michael T. Battista

Douglas H. Clements

Karen Economopoulos

Marlene Kliman

Jan Mokros

Megan Murray

Ricardo Nemirovsky

Andee Rubin

Susan Jo Russell

Cornelia Tierney

Contributing Authors

Mary Berle-Carman

Rebecca B. Corwin

Rebeka Eston

Claryce Evans

Anne Goodrow

Cliff Konold

Chris Mainhart

Sue McMillen

Jerrie Moffet

Tracy Noble

Kim O'Neil

Mark Ogonowski

Julie Sarama

Amy Shulman Weinberg

Margie Singer

Virginia Woolley

Tracey Wright

Contents

Investigations

CURRICULUM

Overview of Program Components

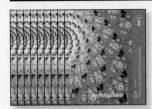

The **Curriculum Units** are the teaching guides. (See far right.)

Implementing Investigations in Grade 2 offers suggestions for implementing the curriculum. It also contains a comprehensive index.

The **Differentiation and Intervention Guide** offers additional activities for each Investigation to support the range of learners.

Investigations for the Interactive Whiteboard provides whole-class instructional support to enhance each session.

The **Resource Masters and Transparencies CD** contains all reproducible materials that support instruction. The **Shapes CD** provides an environment in which students investigate a variety of geometric ideas.

The **Student Activity Book** contains the consumable student pages (Recording Sheets, Homework, Practice, and so on).

The **Student Math Handbook** contains Math Words and Ideas pages and Games directions.

The *Investigations* Curriculum

Investigations in Number, Data, and Space® is a K–5 mathematics curriculum designed to engage students in making sense of mathematical ideas. Six major goals guided the development of the *Investigations in Number, Data, and Space*® curriculum. The curriculum is designed to:

- Support students to make sense of mathematics and learn that they can be mathematical thinkers

- Focus on computational fluency with whole numbers as a major goal of the elementary grades

- Provide substantive work in important areas of mathematics—rational numbers, geometry, measurement, data, and early algebra—and connections among them

- Emphasize reasoning about mathematical ideas

- Communicate mathematics content and pedagogy to teachers

- Engage the range of learners in understanding mathematics

Underlying these goals are three guiding principles that are touchstones for the *Investigations* team as we approach both students and teachers as agents of their own learning:

1. *Students have mathematical ideas.* Students come to school with ideas about numbers, shapes, measurements, patterns, and data. If given the opportunity to learn in an environment that stresses making sense of mathematics, students build on the ideas they already have and learn about new mathematics they have never encountered. Students learn that they are capable of having mathematical ideas, applying what they know to new situations, and thinking and reasoning about unfamiliar problems.

2. *Teachers are engaged in ongoing learning* about mathematics content, pedagogy, and student learning. The curriculum provides material for professional development, to be used by teachers individually or in groups, that supports teachers' continued learning as they use the curriculum over several years. The *Investigations* curriculum materials are designed as much to be a dialogue with teachers as to be a core of content for students.

3. *Teachers collaborate with the students and curriculum materials* to create the curriculum as enacted in the classroom. The only way for a good curriculum to be used well is for teachers to be active participants in implementing it. Teachers use the curriculum to maintain a clear, focused, and coherent agenda for mathematics teaching. At the same time, they observe and listen carefully to students, try to understand how they are thinking, and make teaching decisions based on these observations.

Investigations is based on experience from research and practice, including field testing that involved documentation of thousands of hours in classrooms, observations of students, input from teachers, and analysis of student work. As a result, the curriculum addresses the learning needs of real students in a wide range of classrooms and communities. The investigations are carefully designed to invite all students into mathematics—girls and boys; members of diverse cultural, ethnic, and language groups; and students with a wide variety of strengths, needs, and interests.

Based on this extensive classroom testing, the curriculum takes seriously the time students need to develop a strong conceptual foundation and skills based on that foundation. Each curriculum unit focuses on an area of content in depth, providing time for students to develop and practice ideas across a variety of activities and contexts that build on each other. Daily guidelines for time spent on class sessions, Classroom Routines (K–3), and Ten-Minute Math (3–5) reflect the commitment to devoting adequate time to mathematics in each school day.

About This Curriculum Unit

This **Curriculum Unit** is one of nine teaching guides in Grade 2. The ninth unit in Grade 2 is *Measuring Length and Time*.

- The **Introduction and Overview** section organizes and presents the instructional materials, provides background information, and highlights important features specific to this unit.

- Each Curriculum Unit contains several **Investigations.** Each Investigation focuses on a set of related mathematical ideas.

- Investigations are divided into one-hour **Sessions,** or lessons.

- Sessions have a combination of these parts: **Activity, Discussion, Math Workshop, Assessment Activity,** and **Session Follow-Up.**

- Each session also has one or more **Classroom Routines** that are done outside of math time.

- At the back of the book is a collection of **Teacher Notes** and **Dialogue Boxes** that provide professional development related to the unit.

- Also included at the back of the book are the **Student Math Handbook** pages for this unit.

- The **Index** provides a way to look up important words or terms.

Overview

OF THIS UNIT

Investigation	Session	Day	
INVESTIGATION 1 **Different Units, Different Counts** Students use a variety of nonstandard units and indirect comparison to measure and compare the lengths of different items. They discuss what happens when they measure with different units and then share strategies for measuring accurately. Students also develop strategies for finding the difference between measurements.	**1.1** Scavenger Hunt	1	
	1.2 Scavenger Hunt Workshop	2	
	1.3 Measuring with Different Units	3	
	1.4 Measuring Jumps	4	
	1.5 Comparing Jumps	5	
	1.6 Assessment: A Measurement Disagreement	6	
INVESTIGATION 2 **Creating a Measuring Tool** Students discuss the need to measure objects with a common unit. They create a 12-inch measuring tool and use it to measure lengths, both shorter and longer than 12 inches.	**2.1** The Land of Inch	7	
	2.2 Measuring with the Inch-Brick Tool	8	
	2.3 A Map of the Land of Inch	9	
INVESTIGATION 3 **Two Measurement Systems** Students are introduced to standard measurement tools. They use rulers to measure familiar objects and various lengths, and to locate benchmarks on their bodies that they can use to estimate lengths. Students are introduced to centimeters and meters and find objects that are about equal to these units.	**3.1** Assessment: The King's Foot	10	
	3.2 Rulers and Body Benchmarks	11	
	3.3 Measurement Strategies	12	
	3.4 Moving to Metric	13	
	3.5 Metric Measurement	14	
INVESTIGATION 4 **Representing Time** Students are introduced to timelines as a way to represent time as a horizontal sequence. They use timelines to represent events and to determine the time and duration of events.	**4.1** A Timeline Tells a Story	15	
	4.2 Hours of the Day and Night	16	
	4.3 Fred & Winnipeg Timelines	17	
	4.4 Solving Timeline Problems	18	
	4.5 Special Day Timelines	19	
	4.6 Comparing Special Day Timelines	20	
	4.7 End-of-Unit Assessment	21	

Each *Investigations* session has some combination of these five parts: **Activity, Discussion, Math Workshop, Assessment Activity,** and **Session Follow-Up.** These session parts are indicated in the chart below. Each session also has one **Classroom Routine** that is done outside of math time.

 Ⓦ Interactive Whiteboard

Activity	Discussion	Math Workshop	Assessment Activity	Session Follow-Up
Ⓦ ●	●			●
●	Ⓦ	●		●
Ⓦ	Ⓦ	●		●
	Ⓦ	●		●
●	Ⓦ			●
●	Ⓦ		Ⓦ	●
Ⓦ	Ⓦ Ⓦ			●
	Ⓦ	●		●
Ⓦ	● ●			●
	● ●		Ⓦ	●
●	●	●		●
	Ⓦ ●	●		●
●	Ⓦ	●		●
●	Ⓦ Ⓦ			●
● Ⓦ				●
Ⓦ ●				●
Ⓦ	Ⓦ			●
Ⓦ ● ●				●
Ⓦ Ⓦ ●				●
Ⓦ ●	●			●
			Ⓦ	●

Classroom Routines

Quick Images	Today's Number	How Many Pockets?	What Time Is It?
Ⓦ			
	Ⓦ		
			Ⓦ
Ⓦ			
		Ⓦ	
			Ⓦ
Ⓦ			
		Ⓦ	
			Ⓦ
		Ⓦ	
Ⓦ			
		Ⓦ	
			Ⓦ
Ⓦ			
		Ⓦ	
			Ⓦ
			Ⓦ
			Ⓦ
			Ⓦ
			Ⓦ

Mathematics

Measuring Length and Time is the Grade 2 unit in the measurement strand of *Investigations*. This unit develops ideas about linear measurement as it relates to length, width, and units of measure, and to time, in terms of representing time on a timeline and calculating duration.

LOOKING BACK Young children are often curious about and interested in questions of measurement. It is not unusual to see children comparing heights to find out who is taller nor is it unusual to hear students talking about the sizes of dinosaurs, whales, or tadpoles. However, young students need many opportunities to develop their understanding of the particular attribute they are comparing or measuring. This conceptual development is important for any attribute we measure, whether it is length, area, volume, or even time.

In the Grade 1 unit, *Fish Lengths and Animal Jumps,* students' work focused on measuring length. Students had many opportunities to measure length with a variety of units (paper clips, cubes, tiles, craft sticks) and develop strategies to assure accuracy and reliability. They came to see that if two people measure an object using the same unit, they get the same count; but if they use different-sized units, they get different counts.

Earlier this year in *Parts of a Whole, Parts of a Group* (Unit 7), students worked with basic concepts of fractions and learned how fractions are expressed in words—one half, one fourth (or one quarter), three fourths (or three quarters)—and represented with numbers—$\frac{1}{2}, \frac{1}{4}, \frac{3}{4}$. This fraction work supports students as they encounter partial units of measure such as $3\frac{1}{2}$ inches.

Throughout the year, in the *What Time Is It?* routine, students have explored the clock's face, a complex representation that incorporates different units. They have learned to tell time to the whole, half, and quarter hour, and have also worked with 5-minute intervals of the clock face. They have learned to read and represent these times using analog and digital representations.

This unit focuses on the following Mathematical Emphases:

1 Linear Measurement Understanding length

Math Focus Points

◆ Comparing two lengths

◆ Using direct and indirect comparison to identify equal lengths

◆ Identifying length and width as different dimensions of an object

In *Measuring Length and Time,* students develop their understanding of the concept of length and how length is measured. As they compare lengths of real-world objects, they come to recognize length in many different contexts. Talking about length seems straightforward when considering the length of a pencil or a straight line. However, it becomes more complex when talking about an object that has two dimensions that can be measured (e.g., the length and width of a desktop). Since both of these dimensions have length (note two different meanings for the word *length*), we can measure the length of each dimension. Think about a bookcase and the many line segments it includes—top to bottom, side to side, front to back. Each of these segments has a length; which one we measure depends on our purpose.

Comparing lengths of objects is natural and often spontaneous. Some students compare objects directly by placing them side by side. Others compare indirectly by introducing a third object such as a piece of string. They might compare two objects that cannot be placed next to each other by cutting a string to be placed next to one object, and then comparing the length of that string to the other object.

2 Linear Measurement **Using linear units**

Math Focus Points

- Iterating units to measure length

- Estimating and calculating length using units that are related by a 2:1 ratio

- Identifying strategies for accurate measurement

- Considering sources of measurement error

- Understanding that different-sized units yield different counts (the smaller the unit, the higher the count)

- Establishing the need for and using a common unit in order to compare measurements

- Identifying and labeling partial units

- Recognizing that, given equal counts of two different units, the larger unit marks off a longer length

As students gain experience with length, methods of direct and indirect comparison give way to the more sophisticated strategy of using units that can repeat, such as connecting cubes or craft sticks. Students join the cubes, or repeatedly place the units end to end, and count how many unit lengths "fit" in the length of an object. This method is more sophisticated than direct comparison because it introduces the power of numerical reasoning to work with length. A continuous length is now countable—the number of discrete units that equal the continuous length can be counted. Numerous objects in various locations can be numerically compared. Total length, as well as differences in length, can be found. And lengths can be verbally described and permanently recorded.

When measuring length with units, one does not necessarily have the number of physical units that will fit into the length being measured. Students learn that they can *iterate* the unit, that is, they can repeatedly place the same object (the unit), carefully noting where it ends in one position in order to know where the next placement should begin. Repeatedly placing the unit yields the same count as if they had that number of physical units.

Students need many opportunities to use informal, as well as standard, measuring tools. As they use different units of measure, they begin to learn about the relationship between sizes of units and the results of measuring. That is, when measuring a particular length, the count of the units depends on the size of the unit. Specifically, the smaller the unit, the greater the count; when one unit is half the length of another, the count is doubled. Through discussing their methods, students learn that agreeing on a common unit is critical to communicating measurement information to others and comparing results.

3 Linear Measurement **Measuring with standard units**

Math Focus Points

- Establishing the need for and using a standard unit of measure

- Creating and using a 12-inch measuring tool

- Iterating a 12-inch measuring tool

- Measuring lengths that are longer than 12 inches

- Using a ruler as a standard measuring tool

- Comparing a variety of measuring tools

- Becoming familiar with the terms *inches, feet, yards, centimeters,* and *meters* as standard units of measure

- Using inches, feet, yards, centimeters, and meters to describe lengths

- Comparing centimeters and inches

Tools of measurement, such as rulers and yardsticks, are marked with units of measure and conveniently iterate, making the measurement process easier and more efficient. As children grow from their informal encounters to more structured experiences using tools of measurement, emphasis needs to be placed on developing children's quantitative reasoning to be sure that their use of a measuring tool is based on conceptual understanding and makes sense to them. Children's own construction of tools can foster their understanding not only of the conventional units, but also of the process of measuring with a tool. By constructing measurement tools, children can discover the principles that underlie the design and use of the tool. By comparing their own measuring tools with a conventional ruler, students can identify the unit—an inch as the space between any two consecutive numbers or between the left edge of the ruler and 1—and the meaning of the numbers on a ruler.

In the United States, the conventional units of length are inches, feet, yards, and miles. However, most countries in the world have agreed to use the metric system—centimeters, meters, and kilometers. In the latter part of this unit, students become accustomed to both systems: first, using rulers to measure in inches and feet, and then measuring in centimeters and meters.

4 Time **Representing time and calculating duration**

Math Focus Points

◆ Representing time as a horizontal sequence

◆ Connecting a time, its digital notation, and its representation on an analog clock to a timeline

◆ Naming and using notation for times that are 30 and 15 minutes before or after the hour

◆ Associating times with daily events

◆ Using a timeline to determine duration

◆ Moving forward and backward along a timeline in multiples of hours, half hours, and quarter hours

◆ Using a timeline to show a 24-hour period

◆ Recording events on a timeline

The work in Investigation 4 extends students' work with understanding time, focusing on the idea that time can be represented as a horizontal sequence. In the first session, students represent events from a story in a horizontal sequence that indicates the order of the events. Then students work with timelines, associating events with a particular time. Students start with timelines that show the events of the school day, then gradually expand the timeline both forward and backward until they are working with a timeline that shows a 24-hour cycle.

Much of the work students do in this investigation, in both the sessions and the Classroom Routines, focuses on determining intervals of time. Using timelines and clocks with moveable hands to help them explain their thinking, students consider problems such as: How long is it from the time we come back from lunch at 12:30 until we go to gym at 2:00? In most of the work about intervals, students consider starting and ending times that fall on the hour or half hour. Beginning in Session 4.4, students also consider 15-minute intervals.

By developing their own Special Day Timelines, students work on how to represent duration on a timeline, increase their familiarity with what events occur at different times of the day, and gain experience with the sequence of hours.

This Unit also focuses on

◆ Solving comparison problems by finding the difference between two measurements

Classroom Routines focus on

◆ Developing and analyzing visual images for quantities

◆ Combining groups of 10s and 1s

◆ Using standard notation (+, −, =) to write equations

◆ Generating equivalent expressions for a number

◆ Developing fluency with addition and subtraction

◆ Using standard notation (+, −, =) to record expressions and write equations

◆ Making predictions about data

◆ Collecting, counting, representing, discussing, interpreting, and comparing data

◆ Counting by groups

◆ Developing strategies for solving addition problems with many addends

◆ Using known combinations (i.e., combinations that make 10) to combine numbers

◆ Using a place value model to represent a number as 10s and 1s

◆ Using clocks as tools for keeping track of and measuring time

◆ Naming, notating and telling time to the hour, half hour, and quarter hour on digital and analog clocks

◆ Associating times on the hour and half hour with daily events

◆ Determining what time it will be when given start and elapsed times that are multiples of 15 minutes

◆ Seeing a timeline as a representation of events over time

◆ Using a timeline to keep track of and compare time and events

◆ Determining the length of a given interval (e.g., 8:30 to 9:30) or activity (e.g., math class)

◆ Solving problems involving elapsed time

LOOKING FORWARD

In Grades 3 through 5 students will continue to have opportunities to measure length in a variety of contexts: measuring heights of students in the Grade 3 unit *Surveys and Line Plots,* heights of plants in the Grade 4 unit *Stories, Tables, and Graphs,* and perimeters of different objects in the Grade 3 unit *Perimeters, Angles, and Area.* Strategies for measuring length will be translated into strategies for measuring area and volume in the Grade 3 unit *Solids and Boxes.*

Students will work on telling time to the 5 minutes (2:35, 6:55) in the Grade 3 Ten-Minute Math. In the Grade 3 units *Collections and Travel Stories; Equal Groups;* and *Finding Fair Shares,* they will encounter problems about elapsed time (e.g., How much time has passed from 2:10 to 2:55?).

Representing events along a horizontal line with equal intervals is the basis of later work on representing change over time. In the Grade 3 unit, *Stories, Tables, and Graphs,* students work with graphs of temperature over a day, a week, and a year. They also work with graphs that depict the number of marbles accumulated over a month by children on an imaginary planet. Study of change over time continues in Grades 4 and 5.

Assessment

IN THIS UNIT

ONGOING ASSESSMENT: Observing Students at Work

The following sessions provide **Ongoing Assessment: Observing Students at Work** opportunities:

- **Session 1.1, p. 26**
- **Session 1.2, p. 32**
- **Session 1.3, p. 39**
- **Session 1.4, p. 45**
- **Session 1.5, p. 48**
- **Session 1.6, pp. 52 and 54**
- **Session 2.1, p. 62**

- **Session 2.2, pp. 67, 68, and 69**
- **Session 2.3, p. 72**
- **Session 3.1, p. 82**
- **Session 3.2, pp. 86, 89, and 90**
- **Session 3.3, p. 93**
- **Session 3.4, pp. 98 and 100**
- **Session 3.5, p. 103**

- **Session 4.1, p. 115**
- **Session 4.2, pp. 118 and 119**
- **Session 4.3, p. 123**
- **Session 4.4, pp. 128, 130, and 132**
- **Session 4.5, pp. 135 and 138**
- **Session 4.6, p. 141**
- **Session 4.7, p. 144**

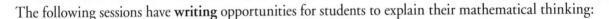

WRITING OPPORTUNITIES

The following sessions have **writing** opportunities for students to explain their mathematical thinking:

- **Session 1.1, p. 27**
  Student Activity Book, p. 2

- **Session 1.2, p. 31**
  Student Activity Book, p. 5

- **Session 3.2, p. 86**
  Student Activity Book, p. 32

- **Session 3.3, p. 93**
  Student Activity Book, p. 39

- **Session 3.3, p. 95**
  Student Activity Book, pp. 41 and 42

- **Session 3.4, p. 99**
  Student Activity Book, p. 44

- **Session 3.5, p. 102**
  Student Activity Book, p. 47

- **Session 4.4, p. 131**
  Student Activity Book, p. 63

PORTFOLIO OPPORTUNITIES

The following sessions have work appropriate for a **portfolio:**

- **Session 1.6, p. 52**
  Student Activity Book, p. 17

- **Session 1.6, p. 53**
  M6, Assessment: A Measurement Disagreement

- **Session 3.1, p. 82**
  M13, Assessment: The King's Foot

- **Session 3.3, p. 93**
  Student Activity Book, p. 39

- **Session 3.4, p. 99**
  Student Activity Book, p. 44

- **Session 4.1, p. 111**
  M18, *Today's Number: 72*

- **Session 4.4, p. 131**
  Student Activity Book, p. 63

- **Session 4.7, pp. 144–145**
  M32–M35, End-of-Unit Assessment

Assessing the Benchmarks

Observing students as they engage in conversation about their ideas is a primary means to assess their mathematical understanding. Consider all of your students' work, not just the written assessments. See the chart below for suggestions about key activities to observe.

See the **Differentiation and Intervention Guide** for quizzes that can be used after each Investigation.

Benchmarks in This Unit	Key Activities to Observe	Assessment
1. Identify sources of measurement error.	**Sessions 1.2–1.3:** Scavenger Hunt Discussions **Sessions 1.3–1.5:** Comparing Jumps **Session 2.1:** The Land of Inch	**Session 1.6 Assessment Activity:** A Measurement Disagreement
2. Recognize that the same count of different-sized units yields different lengths.	**Session 3.1:** Measuring with Footlengths	**Session 3.1 Assessment Activity:** The King's Foot
3. Recognize that, when measuring the same length, larger units yield smaller counts.	**Sessions 1.4–1.5:** Comparing Jumps **Session 2.1:** The Land of Inch	**Session 1.6 Assessment Activity:** A Measurement Disagreement **Session 3.1 Assessment Activity:** The King's Foot **Session 4.7 End-of-Unit Assessment:** Problem 1 Inches and Centimeters
4. Measure objects using inches and centimeters. 5. Use a ruler to measure lengths longer than one foot.	**Session 2.2:** Measuring Clothes, Buildings and Jumps in the Land of Inch **Session 2.3:** Maps of the Land of Inch **Session 3.2:** Measure and Compare **Session 3.3:** Measuring Our Classroom **Session 3.5:** Measuring with Inches and Centimeters	**Session 4.7 End-of-Unit Assessment:** Problem 1 Inches and Centimeters
6. Solve problems involving the beginning time of an event, ending time of an event, and duration of the event; given two of these, find the third for events beginning and ending on the hour or half hour.	**Session 4.4:** How Long Is It? **Session 4.4:** Solving Timeline Problems **Session 4.5:** Special Day Timelines	**Session 4.7 End-of-Unit Assessment:** Problem 2 Chris's Story Timeline Problems
7. Use a timeline to record and determine duration to the hour or half hour.	**Session 4.3:** Fred & Winnipeg Timelines **Session 4.4:** Solving Timeline Problems	**Session 4.7 End-of-Unit Assessment:** Problem 2 Chris's Story Timeline Problems

Relating the Mathematical Emphases to the Benchmarks

Mathematical Emphases	Benchmarks
Linear Measurement Understanding length	1
Linear Measurement Using linear unit	2, 3
Linear Measurement Measuring with standard units	4, 5
Time Representing time and calculating duration	6

Classroom Routines

Classroom Routines offer practice and review of key concepts for this grade level. These daily activities, to be done in ten minutes outside of math class, occur in a regular rotation every 4–5 days. Specific directions for the day's routine are provided in each session. For the full description and variations of each classroom routine see *Implementing Investigations in Grade 2*.

Quick Images

Students combine groups of 10s and 1s to determine the total number of squares in an image and use standard notation to write equations that represent the arrangement.

Math Focus Points

◆ Developing and analyzing visual images for quantities

◆ Combining groups of 10s and 1s

◆ Using standard notation $(+, -, =)$ to write equations

How Many Pockets?

Students work individually to record the class's pocket data on a class list and calculate the amount of money the pockets are worth if each pocket is worth 1¢, 5¢, or 10¢.

Math Focus Points

◆ Making predictions about data

◆ Collecting, counting, representing, discussing, interpreting, and comparing data

◆ Counting by groups

◆ Developing strategies for solving addition problems with many addends

◆ Using known combinations (i.e., combinations that make 10) to combine numbers

◆ Using a place value model to represent a number as 10s and 1s

Today's Number

Students generate *Today's Number* using subtraction and two or more numbers.

Math Focus Points

◆ Generating equivalent expressions for a number

◆ Developing fluency with addition and subtraction

◆ Using standard notation $(+, -, =)$ to record expressions and write equations

What Time Is It?

Students practice telling time to the hour, half hour, and quarter hour. They determine what time it will be in 30-, 60-, and 90-minute intervals, and practice naming and notating these times. Students also use a timeline to answer questions about duration.

Math Focus Points

◆ Using clocks as tools for keeping track of and measuring time

◆ Naming, notating and telling time to the hour, half hour, and quarter hour on digital and analog clocks

◆ Associating times on the hour and half hour with daily events

◆ Determining what time it will be when given start and elapsed times that are multiples of 15 minutes

◆ Seeing a timeline as a representation of events over time

◆ Using a timeline to keep track of and compare time and events

◆ Determining the length of a given interval (e.g., 8:30 to 9:30) or activity (e.g., math class)

◆ Solving problems involving elapsed time

Practice and Review

Practice and review play a critical role in the *Investigations* program. The following components and features are available to provide regular reinforcement of key mathematical concepts and procedures.

Books	Features	In This Unit . . .
Curriculum Unit	**Classroom Routines** offer practice and review of key concepts for this grade level. These daily activities, to be done in ten minutes outside of math class, occur in a regular rotation every 4–5 days. Specific directions for the day's routine are provided in each session. For the full description and variations of each classroom routine see *Implementing Investigations in Grade 2*.	• **All sessions**
Student Activity Book	**Daily Practice** pages in the *Student Activity Book* provide one of three types of written practice: **reinforcement** of the content of the unit, **ongoing review,** or **enrichment** opportunities. Some Daily Practice pages will also have Ongoing Review items with multiple-choice problems similar to those on standardized tests.	• **All sessions**
	Homework pages in the *Student Activity Book* are an extension of the work done in class. At times they help students prepare for upcoming activities.	• **Session 1.2** • **Session 3.4** • **Session 1.3** • **Session 4.1** • **Session 2.2** • **Session 4.2** • **Session 3.2** • **Session 4.4** • **Session 3.3**
Student Math Handbook	**Math Words and Ideas** in the *Student Math Handbook* are pages that summarize key words and ideas. Most Words and Ideas pages have at least one exercise.	• **Student Math Handbook, pp. 73–75, 134, 136–156**
	Games pages are found in a section of the *Student Math Handbook*.	• **No games are introduced in this unit.**

Supporting the Range of Learners

The **Differentiation and Intervention Guide** provides Intervention, Extension, and Practice activities for use within each Investigation.

Sessions	1.1	1.2	1.3	1.4	1.5	1.6	2.1	2.2	2.3	3.1	3.2	3.3	4.2	4.3	4.4	4.5	4.6
Intervention	•	•	•		•	•	•	•	•		•	•	•	•	•	•	
Extension		•		•				•			•	•		•			
ELL	•							•		•		•					•

Intervention

Suggestions are made to support and engage students who are having difficulty with a particular idea, activity, or problem.

Extension

Suggestions are made to support and engage students who finish early or may be ready for additional challenge.

English Language Learners (ELL)

English Language Learners may need extra support as they learn the names and functions of various measurement tools, including strips of adding machine paper, cubes, "inch-bricks," rulers, yardsticks, tape measures, timelines, and analog clocks.

In previous units, students used comparatives and superlatives to describe the size of objects (*big/bigger/biggest; small/smaller/smallest*). In this unit, they compare length (*long/longer/longest; short/shorter/shortest*) and time (*early/earlier/earliest; late/later/latest*). Practice of comparatives and superlatives will help English Language Learners apply these language structures to new vocabulary.

English Language Learners may also need help with common time-related terms such as *before, after, between, first, then, next,* and *until*. Show students a simple timeline of daily events to illustrate these words in context. Here's a *timeline* of my morning routine. *First,* I wake up, get dressed, and eat breakfast. *Then* I brush my teeth. *Next,* I go outside and wait for the bus. I ride the bus from 7:00 *until* 7:30, when I get to school. *Between* 7:30 and 8:00, I get the classroom ready. *Then* I wait for my students to arrive. Ask students some questions to assess their understanding. What's the *first* thing I do in the morning? What's the *last* thing I do before I leave home? What do I do *earlier*—eat breakfast or ride the bus? What do I do *between* 7:30 and 8:00? Then students can make simple timelines of their own morning routines and explain them to each other. Encourage English Language Learners to use the target vocabulary as much as possible.

Working with the Range of Learners is a set of episodes written by teachers that focuses on meeting the needs of the range of learners in the classroom. In the first section, *Setting up the Mathematical Community,* teachers write about how they create a supportive and productive learning environment in their classrooms. In the next section, *Accommodations for Learning,* teachers focus on specific modifications they make to meet the needs of some of their learners. In the last section, *Language and Representation,* teachers share how they help students use representations and develop language to investigate and express mathematical ideas. The questions at the end of each case provide a starting point for your own reflection or for discussion with colleagues. See *Implementing Investigations in Grade 2* for this set of episodes.

Mathematical Emphases

Linear Measurement Understanding length

Math Focus Points

◆ Comparing two lengths

◆ Using direct and indirect comparison to identify equal lengths

Linear Measurement Using linear units

Math Focus Points

◆ Iterating units to measure length

◆ Estimating and calculating length using units that are related by a 2:1 ratio

◆ Identifying strategies for accurate measurement

◆ Considering sources of measurement error

◆ Understanding that different-sized units yield different counts (the smaller the unit, the higher the count)

◆ Establishing the need for and using a common unit in order to compare measurements

This Investigation also focuses on

◆ Solving comparison problems by finding the difference between two measurements

Different Units, Different Counts

	Student Activity Book	Student Math Handbook	Professional Development: Read Ahead of Time	
SESSION 1.1 p. 24				
Scavenger Hunt Students find items that are about the same length as each of several strips of adding machine tape. By indirect comparison, they compare the length of the items with the length of the strips, and record each length. Students share strategies for comparing lengths.	1–3	146	• **Mathematics in this Unit,** p. 10 • **Teacher Note:** Learning to Measure Length, p. 147 • **Dialogue Box:** Matching Lengths, p. 165	
SESSION 1.2 p. 29				
Scavenger Hunt Workshop Students work on two Scavenger Hunt activities during Math Workshop. In Scavenger Hunt 1, they find objects that are about the same length as each of several strips. In Scavenger Hunt 2, they measure objects using 2 different lengths of paper strips that have a 2-to-1 ratio.	1–2, 4–8	146, 147, 148	• **Dialogue Box:** Using Related Units of Measure, p. 166; What's the Length and What's the Width?, p. 167	
SESSION 1.3 p. 36				
Measuring with Different Units In Math Workshop, students measure different lengths with a variety of nonstandard units. The class discussion of Scavenger Hunt 2 addresses the result of measuring with different units and identifies strategies for accurate measurement.	4–5, 9–11	147, 148	• **Teacher Note:** Measuring and Comparing: How Far Can You Jump?, p. 149	

Classroom Routines See page 16 for an overview.

Quick Images

- T82, *Quick Images 1: Tens and Ones* 🖨 Cut apart the images.
- T83, *Quick Images 2: Tens and Ones* 🖨 Cut apart the images.

Today's Number

- **No materials needed**

What Time Is It?

- **Student clocks** (1 per pair)
- **Demonstration clock**

Materials to Gather	Materials to Prepare
• **Rolls of adding machine tape** (4–6 rolls) • **String or ribbon** (several rolls) • **Connecting cubes** (class set) • **Craft sticks** (200–300)	• **Paper strips** Cut 2 or more identical sets of 6 strips of adding machine tape in lengths that match items in your classroom, such as the width of a bookshelf or the height of a wastebasket. The shorter lengths should vary by 3–6 inches; longer by 10–12 inches. Label the strips A through F. Post one set of strips horizontally at a height accessible to students and another set on the floor. • **M1–M2, Family Letter** Make copies. (1 per student)
• **Basket or container** • **Common objects** such as a pencil, paintbrush, tissue box, or a book (4–6) One object should be about the same length as one blue strip. • **Materials for Scavenger Hunt 1** See Session 1.1. • **Envelopes** (1 per pair)	• **Measuring strips** Cut 6″ x 1″ blue paper strips and 3″ x 1″ yellow paper strips from construction paper. Prepare enough strips so that each pair has 5 blue and 20 yellow strips and you have a few extras. For durability, strips can be laminated and saved from year to year. Place each pair's strips in an envelope for easy distribution. • **Chart paper** Divide the chart paper into 6 columns and label them "Strip A," "Strip B," "Strip C," "Strip D," "Strip E," and "Strip F." Title the chart: "What's as Long as the Paper Strips?" • **M4, Measuring Strips** Make copies. (1 per student)
• **Rolls of adding machine tape** (4–6 rolls) • **Scissors** (1 per pair) • **Masking tape** (as needed) • **Craft sticks** (200–300) • **Measuring strips** (from Session 1.2)	• **Starting lines** Use masking tape or electrical tape, which is easier to remove from floors and rugs, to create 2–3 starting lines for the How Far Can You Jump? activity.

🖨 Overhead Transparency

Different Units, Different Counts, *continued*

SESSION 1.4	p. 43	Student Activity Book	Student Math Handbook	Professional Development: Read Ahead of Time	
Measuring Jumps In Math Workshop, students measure their jumps using iterated units and solve measurement story problems. Based on their measurements, students discuss whether they can compare their jumps since they measured with different units.		9; 13–14	147, 150–151, 152		
SESSION 1.5 p. 47					
Comparing Jumps Students measure their jumps again, this time using cubes. They examine the class results and explain why they can now compare their jumps when they could not compare them in the previous session.		15–16	150–151, 152		
SESSION 1.6 p. 51					
Assessment: A Measurement Disagreement Students find the difference between the longest jump in the class and the shortest and come together to discuss their strategies. The investigation concludes with an assessment.		17–18	148, 150–151	• **Teacher Note:** Assessment: A Measurement Disagreement, p. 150	

Materials to Gather	Materials to Prepare
• **Materials for How Far Can You Jump?** See Session 1.3. • **Scissors** (1 per pair) • **Masking tape** (as needed) • **Craft sticks** (200–300) • **Measuring strips** (from Session 1.2)	• **Chart paper** Divide the chart paper into 3 columns and label them "Name," "Longest Jump," and "Shortest Jump." Title the chart "Longest Jump/Shortest Jump."
• **Connecting cubes** (class set) • **Students' strips of jump lengths** (from Session 1.3)	• **Chart paper** Divide the chart paper into 3 columns and label them "Name," "Longest Jump," and "Shortest Jump." Title the chart "Measuring Our Jumps with Cubes."
• **Connecting cubes** (class set) • **Chart: "Measuring Our Jumps with Cubes"** (from Session 1.5)	• **M6, Assessment: A Measurement Disagreement** Make copies. (1 per student) • **M7–M8, Family Letter** Make copies. (1 per student)

Scavenger Hunt

Math Focus Points

◆ Comparing two lengths

◆ Using direct and indirect comparison to identify equal lengths

Vocabulary

length
width

Today's Plan		Materials
ACTIVITY **① Introducing Scavenger Hunt 1**	🕐 10 MIN 👥 CLASS 🤝 PAIRS	• *Student Activity Book*, pp. 1–2 • Strips of adding machine tape*; rolls of adding machine tape; string or ribbon; connecting cubes; craft sticks
ACTIVITY **② Scavenger Hunt 1**	🕐 40 MIN 🤝 PAIRS	• *Student Activity Book*, pp. 1–2 • Materials from Activity 1
DISCUSSION **③ Sharing Strategies**	🕐 10 MIN 👥 CLASS	• Materials from Activity 1
SESSION FOLLOW-UP **④ Daily Practice**		• *Student Activity Book*, p. 3 • *Student Math Handbook*, p. 146 • M1–M2, Family Letter*

*See *Materials to Prepare*, p. 21.

Classroom Routines

Quick Images: Tens and Ones Show Image A from *Quick Images 1: Tens and Ones* (T82). Follow the basic *Quick Images* activity. Ask students to determine the total number of squares and share their strategies. Record equations to represent the image, such as $10 + 10 + 10 + 5 = 35$, or $40 - 5 = 35$. Repeat for Images B and C.

ACTIVITY

1 Introducing Scavenger Hunt 1

10 MIN **CLASS** **PAIRS**

Look at the paper strips I have displayed around the room. What can you tell about the strips just by looking at them?

Students might say:

"This strip over here is the shortest one."

"All the strips are different lengths."

The strips are all different lengths, and we're going to use them in a scavenger hunt. You will work with partners to find things in the classroom that are about the same length as each strip.

You might want to explain that a scavenger hunt is a game where people find different things that are on a list. Point out one of the longest strips, and ask students to suggest some things that might be about the same length as the strip.

Yes, [the length of the bookcase or the width of the classroom door] might be about the same length as this paper strip. Your job will be to find things in the classroom that are about the same length as the strips. You cannot move the strips—the strips are to stay where I have put them—but you can use materials in the classroom to help you.❶

Students use connecting cubes to measure the length of strip A.

Math Note

❶ **About the Same Length** Emphasize that items students find for each strip should be about the same length as the strips; they do not have to be exactly the same length. To help students develop a sense of what "about the same length" means, compare the lengths of two objects to one of the strips you have posted. Make the length of one object clearly different from that of the strip, while the other object is about the same length as the strip.

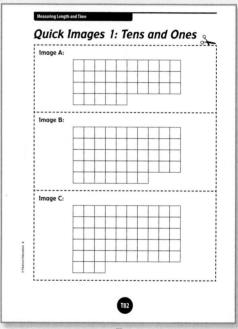

Measuring Length and Time

Quick Images 1: Tens and Ones

Image A:

Image B:

Image C:

T82

© Pearson Education 2

▲ **Transparencies, T82**

Professional Development

❷ Teacher Note: Learning to Measure Length, p. 147

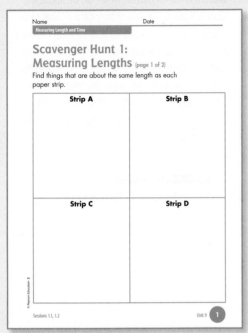

Name _____ Date _____

Measuring Length and Time

Scavenger Hunt 1:
Measuring Lengths (page 1 of 2)

Find things that are about the same length as each paper strip.

Strip A	Strip B
Strip C	**Strip D**

Sessions 1.1, 1.2 — Unit 9 — 1

▲ Student Activity Book, p. 1

Students work with a partner to find a way to compare the length (or width) of things in the classroom to the paper strips. Show students the measuring materials they might use, such as string, adding machine tape, connecting cubes, or craft sticks. For at least three of the strips, they should find several items that measure the same length. Each student records on *Student Activity Book* pages 1–2.

ACTIVITY

❷ Scavenger Hunt 1

40 MIN   PAIRS

As you circulate among students, note how they are comparing the lengths of the strips with the lengths of the objects.❷

A student uses craft sticks to measure the width of a book and then compares the width to a strip.

ONGOING ASSESSMENT: Observing Students at Work

Students use direct and indirect measurement techniques to compare lengths of objects and strips.

- **How do students compare lengths to the shortest strips?**
  Do they use direct comparison? Do they hold objects next to short strips to compare lengths?

- **How do students compare longer lengths?** Do they use indirect comparison strategies? For example, do they cut a length of string that matches a long strip and use it to compare the strip to another length?

- **Do students use nonstandard units to compare lengths?** For instance, do they measure a strip with connecting cubes, and then use the cube train to find equal lengths? If students use other, noncontinuous units (units that are not easily linked), such as craft sticks, how do they use these units? Do they line units end to end? Do they place the units without gaps or overlaps? Do they repeatedly place only one unit along each length, keeping track of how many times they do so?

- **Are students flexible in their use of materials and methods?** Do they use strategies that "fit" the task? For example, for short lengths, direct comparison often works well and may be more efficient than indirect comparison or using unconventional units.

DIFFERENTIATION: Supporting the Range of Learners

Intervention Some students may benefit from using materials such as connecting cubes, which allow individual units to be linked together. You can also suggest that they use string or adding machine tape. It is likely and expected that students will vary considerably in their ability to iterate a single unit. They will work on this skill throughout this unit.

ELL To participate in this activity, English Language Learners must understand how the word *about* is used in this context. You can demonstrate the meaning with a small group of English Language Learners. Hand out a 12-inch ruler to each student.

Let's find an object that's *about* the same length as this ruler.

Let's look at this 3-hole punch. [Place 3-hole punch above the ruler.] This is a little shorter than the ruler. It is *about* the same length as the ruler.

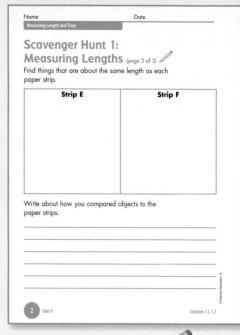

Name _____ Date _____
Measuring Length and Time

Scavenger Hunt 1: Measuring Lengths (page 2 of 2)
Find things that are about the same length as each paper strip.

Strip E	Strip F

Write about how you compared objects to the paper strips.

_____
_____
_____
_____
_____

2 Unit 9   Sessions 1.1, 1.2

▲ **Student Activity Book, p. 2** WRITING

DISCUSSION
3 Sharing Strategies

10 MIN   CLASS

Math Focus Points for Discussion

◆ Comparing two lengths

Students share their strategies for comparing lengths, giving them an opportunity to consider different strategies when they continue the Scavenger Hunt in the following session.

Professional Development

❸ **Dialogue Box:** Matching Lengths, p. 165

Teaching Note

❹ **Save the Paper Strips** Leave the strips posted, so students can continue this activity during Math Workshop in Sessions 1.2, 1.3, and 1.4.

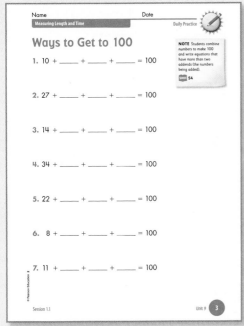

Name _____ Date _____

Measuring Length and Time

Daily Practice

Ways to Get to 100

NOTE Students combine numbers to make 100 and write equations that have more than two addends (the numbers being added).

SMH 54

1. 10 + _____ + _____ + _____ = 100

2. 27 + _____ + _____ + _____ = 100

3. 14 + _____ + _____ + _____ = 100

4. 34 + _____ + _____ + _____ = 100

5. 22 + _____ + _____ + _____ = 100

6. 8 + _____ + _____ + _____ = 100

7. 11 + _____ + _____ + _____ = 100

Session 1.1   Unit 9   3

▲ **Student Activity Book, p. 3**

This brief discussion is intended to give students ideas of different ways to compare lengths.❸ Select one of the longer strips for which students used various strategies.

What did you find to be the same length as Strip [B]?

Have students describe their strategies to find objects that are the same length as Strip B. If someone used a length of string (or some other flexible material) that matches a long strip to compare to another object, have that student demonstrate the strategy. If someone used nonstandard units (cubes, craft sticks, etc.), have that student demonstrate the strategy.❹

Students use a piece of string to measure the length of strip B.

SESSION FOLLOW-UP

 4 **Daily Practice**

 Daily Practice: For ongoing review, have students complete *Student Activity Book* page 3.

 Student Math Handbook: Students and families may use *Student Math Handbook* page 146 for reference and review. See pages 172–178 in the back of this unit.

Family Letter: Send home copies of the Family Letter (M1–M2).

Scavenger Hunt Workshop

Math Focus Points

◆ Using direct and indirect comparison to identify equal lengths

◆ Iterating units to measure length

◆ Estimating and calculating length using units that are related by a 2:1 ratio

◆ Identifying strategies for accurate measurement

Vocabulary

measure	length
estimate	width
	height

Today's Plan			Materials
① ACTIVITY **Introducing Scavenger Hunt 2: Blue and Yellow Strips**	10 MIN	CLASS	• *Student Activity Book*, pp. 4–5 • Basket or bin containing 4–6 common objects, such as a pencil, paintbrush, tissue box, or a book*; blue and yellow measuring strips*
② MATH WORKSHOP **Scavenger Hunt Workshop** **②A** Scavenger Hunt 1 **②B** Scavenger Hunt 2: Blue and Yellow Strips		35 MIN	**②A** • *Student Activity Book*, pp. 1–2 (from Session 1.1) • Materials from Session 1.1, p. 24 **②B** • *Student Activity Book*, pp. 4–5 • Blue and yellow measuring strips* (1 set per pair); materials from Activity 1
③ DISCUSSION **Sharing Measuring Strategies**	15 MIN	CLASS	• Strips of adding machine tape and measuring tools (from Session 1.1); chart paper: What's As Long As the Paper Strips?*
④ SESSION FOLLOW-UP **Daily Practice and Homework**			• *Student Activity Book*, pp. 6–8 • *Student Math Handbook*, pp. 146, 147, 148 • M4*

*See *Materials to Prepare*, p. 21.

Classroom Routines

Today's Number: 49 Using Subtraction Individually, students generate expressions for 49 using only subtraction and two numbers, for example 50 − 1 and 69 − 20. Collect a number of examples on the board and discuss one or two patterns such as 59 − 10, 69 − 20, 79 − 30 or 50 − 1, 51 − 2, 52 − 3 as a whole class.

Math Note

① A 2-to-1 Relationship Do not explicitly tell students that there is a 2-to-1 relationship between the lengths of the strips. Even if a student points it out, refrain from elaborating on the observation until most students have had a chance to work through the activity.

▲ **Student Activity Book, p. 4**

ACTIVITY

Introducing Scavenger Hunt 2: Blue and Yellow Strips

Post a 6″ blue paper strip and a 3″ yellow paper strip side by side on the board.

Have at hand several blue and yellow strips as well as a few objects, such as a paintbrush or pencil that you will use for demonstration purposes.

Remind students of the work they did in the first scavenger hunt activity.

Today in Math Workshop, you will have a chance to work on a different Scavenger Hunt activity. In this hunt, you will measure with these blue and yellow strips. You will work with a partner to find things that are a certain number of blue strips long. For example, suppose I had to find an object from this basket that was about one blue strip long. Which object do you think is about one blue strip long?

From your collection of objects, have a student find an item that is about one blue strip long.

A student shares an object that is about 1 blue strip long.

Next you will have to estimate how many yellow strips long this same object is. What do you think? Look at the yellow strip and then look at this [pencil]. *About* how many yellow strips long is it? ①

Have a student estimate how many yellow strips long it will be, and then measure to check. Explain to students that they will record this information on *Student Activity Book* pages 4–5.

In this Scavenger Hunt you will be looking for objects in our classroom that are about as long as a certain number of blue strips.

Talk through one more example together, discussing with students how they will record on their papers the object, their estimate of the length in yellow strips, and their actual measurement in yellow strips.

MATH WORKSHOP

2 Scavenger Hunt Workshop

35 MIN

If students did not finish Scavenger Hunt 1 during Session 1.1, they should complete the activity so that they can participate in the class discussion at the end of this session.

Students will have an opportunity to continue with Scavenger Hunt 2 in the following session.

2A Scavenger Hunt 1

PAIRS

For complete details about this activity, see Session 1.1, page 25. In preparation for the discussion at the end of this session, identify students who measured with the following:

- Tape or string
- Cubes linked together
- Nonconnecting individual units, such as craft sticks

You will ask these students to share during the discussion.

DIFFERENTIATION: Supporting the Range of Learners

Intervention Students who are relying on direct comparison techniques for measuring may benefit from being shown how to use cubes or string to measure an object indirectly. Work through one example together and then have them try on their own as you observe.

Extension For students who finish early, pose problems such as the following:

- Could my desk fit through the door?
- Could we move the bookshelf into the space next to the game shelf?

Have students tell how they could figure out these problems without moving the objects.

Name _____ *Date* _____
Measuring Length and Time

Scavenger Hunt 2:
How Many Paper Strips? (page 2 of 2)

Blue Strips	Yellow Strips
Find something 6 blue strips long. Object: _____	How many yellow strips is the object? Estimate: _____ Measure: _____
Find something 7 blue strips long. Object: _____	How many yellow strips is the object? Estimate: _____ Measure: _____
Find something 10 blue strips long. Object: _____	How many yellow strips is the object? Estimate: _____ Measure: _____

What did you notice about the number of blue strips compared to the number of yellow strips?

_____

© Pearson Education 2

Sessions 1.2, 1.3   Unit 9   5

▲ **Student Activity Book, p. 5**

Math Note

② **Practice Iterating** For Scavenger Hunt 2, some problems require more blue strips than pairs of students have. Encourage students to find things that are 6, 7, and 10 blue strips long *without* borrowing strips from another pair of students. These problems help students to move away from lining up units end to end and to move toward repeatedly iterating a unit of measure.

Professional Development

❸ **Dialogue Box:** Using Related Units of Measure, p. 166

2B Scavenger Hunt 2: Blue and Yellow Strips

PAIRS

Students work on Scavenger Hunt 2, following the procedure on page 30. At the bottom of *Student Activity Book* page 5, they write about what they noticed as they used the blue and yellow strips to measure.**②❸**

Students use units with a 2:1 ratio to estimate and measure.

ONGOING ASSESSMENT: Observing Students at Work

Students measure objects with blue and yellow paper strips. The lengths of the two strips are related by a ratio of 2:1.

- **How do students measure with the paper units?** Do they align the end of the first strip with the edge of the item and then place several of the strips end to end? Are the strips placed without overlap or gaps between strips?

- **How do students measure objects that require more strips than they have available?**

- **How do students estimate how many of the smaller strips it will take to measure the length of an object?** Do they use the 2-to-1 relationship that exists between the longer and shorter strips, and double the number used for blue strips? Do they visualize how the smaller strips might fit along the item?

DIFFERENTIATION: Supporting the Range of Learners

Intervention For students who are having difficulty estimating the number of yellow strips, suggest that they place two or three yellow strips along the object, and then predict how many.

Intervention Some students may treat each task as a new and different problem. Without telling them about the 2-to-1 relationship, encourage these students to think about how many blue and yellow strips they have used in one problem before they make their next prediction.

- You found that the table was three blue strips or six yellow strips long. If you know the shelf is four blue strips wide, do you have an idea about how many yellow strips it will be?

Extension Have students who complete this activity early measure new objects with the yellow strips and predict how many blue strips long the object is.

DISCUSSION

3 Sharing Measuring Strategies

15 MIN   CLASS

Math Focus Points for Discussion

◆ Identifying strategies for accurate measurement

In preparation for this discussion, post one set of the adding machine strips labeled A–F on the board next to the "What's As Long As The Paper Strips?" chart that you prepared ahead of time.

What's As Long As The Paper Strips?					
Strip A	Strip B	Strip C	Strip D	Strip E	Strip F

Focus the first part of this discussion on any discrepancies that might exist. On the chart, list the names of the objects that students found to be as long as each strip.❹

Professional Development

5 **Dialogue Box:** What's the Length and What's the Width?, p. 167

Name Date

Measuring Length and Time

Daily Practice

How Many Strips?

A class measured with red and green paper strips. All the red strips were the same length. All the green strips were the same length. Use the measurements for the teacher's desk to figure out the missing measurements.

NOTE Students look at measurements to find the relationship between different units.

SMH 150–151

Object	Measurement in Red Strips	Measurement in Green Strips
1. Teacher's desk	10 red strips	5 green strips
2. Student's desk	4 red strips	____ green strips
3. Chalkboard	26 red strips	____ green strips
4. Dictionary	____ red strips	1 green strip
5. Aquarium	____ red strips	4 green strips

Ongoing Review

6. 17 + ____ = 22

(A) 7 (B) 9 (C) 3 (D) 5

© Pearson Education 2

6 Unit 9 Session 1.2

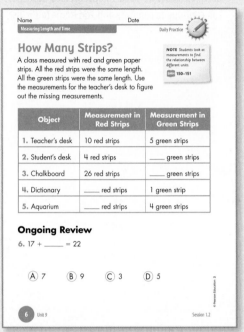

▲ Student Activity Book, p. 6

Name Date

Measuring Length and Time

Measuring Strips

These measuring strips are the same lengths as the blue and yellow strips that you used in school. Cut them out and use them for your work at home. Be sure to save these strips. You will use them again.

blue

blue

blue

yellow yellow yellow yellow yellow yellow

© Pearson Education 2

M4 Unit 9 Sessions 1.2, 1.3, 3.2

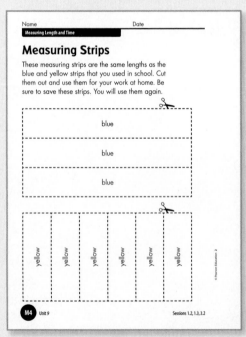

▲ Resource Masters, M4

If discrepancies arise because one object is listed in two different places, discuss why this might be and whether it is possible for the same object to match two different strips. For instance, one student may have found that one object is the same length as Strip [A], while another student found that the same object matches the length of Strip [D]. Different results may be due to errors in measurement technique, such as miscounting the nonstandard units used or failing to align units end to end. However, discrepancies may also arise because students have focused on different dimensions of the object. Ask the students who contributed these results which part of the object they measured. Use this opportunity to clarify the words length, width, and height. 5 Students will have repeated experiences with these dimensions throughout the unit.

Focus the second part of the discussion on measurement strategies.

I noticed that when you were measuring the paper strips, some of you measured with one long thing, such as string or adding machine paper, while other people used smaller things, such as craft sticks or cubes.

Ask three different students to show how they matched a paper strip to an object. Choose a student who used

- Tape or string;
- Cubes linked together;
- Nonconnecting individual units, such as craft sticks.

Make sure to point out such issues as measuring in a straight line, placing units without gaps or overlaps, starting at one end of the object and finishing at the other.

One part of measuring accurately is making sure that you are measuring the correct part of the object. Another part of measuring accurately has to do with where you begin to measure and where you end.

Ask students to comment about this.

Some of you used one long string to measure the strip and then found a matching object, while others used cubes or craft sticks to measure. Which was easier?

Students might say:

"The string is easier because it is just one piece; you don't have to count."

"I like the cubes because they link together. But it's more cubes to count than craft sticks."

"With cubes you don't have to worry about measuring straight or having space in between like you do with the craft sticks."

Suggest to students that they might want to try one of the measurement strategies suggested in this discussion when they work on these activities in the next session.

SESSION FOLLOW-UP

4 Daily Practice and Homework

 Daily Practice: For reinforcement of this unit's content, have students complete *Student Activity Book* page 6.

 Student Math Handbook: Students and families may use *Student Math Handbook* pages 146, 147, 148 for reference and review. See pages 172–178 in the back of this unit.

 Homework: Have students conduct a scavenger hunt at home, similar to the one they've worked on at school. They cut out (and color, if desired) the strips on Measuring Strips (M4), and use them to conduct their hunt. They record their work on *Student Activity Book* pages 7–8.

▲ **Student Activity Book, p. 7**

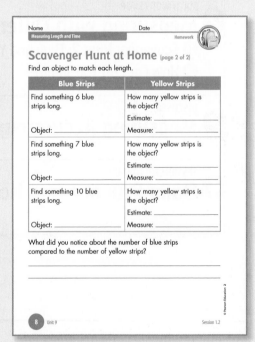

▲ **Student Activity Book, p. 8**

Measuring with Different Units

Math Focus Points

◆ Iterating units to measure length

◆ Considering sources of measurement error

◆ Estimating and calculating length using units that are related by a 2:1 ratio

◆ Identifying strategies for accurate measurement

Vocabulary

unit

Today's Plan

	Materials
① ACTIVITY **Introducing How Far Can You Jump?** 🕐 10 MIN 👥 CLASS	• *Student Activity Book*, p. 9 • Rolls of adding machine tape; scissors; masking tape*; craft sticks; blue and yellow measuring strips (from Session 1.2)
② MATH WORKSHOP **Measuring with Different Units** **2A** Scavenger Hunt 2: Blue and Yellow Strips **2B** How Far Can You Jump? 🕐 35 MIN	**2A** • Materials from Session 1.2, p. 29 **2B** • *Student Activity Book*, p. 9 • Materials from Activity 1
③ DISCUSSION **Measuring Accurately** 🕐 15 MIN 👥 CLASS	• Blue and yellow measuring strips (from Session 1.2)
④ SESSION FOLLOW-UP **Daily Practice and Homework**	• *Student Activity Book*, pp. 10–11 • *Student Math Handbook*, pp. 147, 148 • M4 (from Session 1.2)

*See *Materials to Prepare*, p. 21.

Classroom Routines

What Time Is It?: What Time Will It Be? Write 9:45 on the board. Ask students to set their clocks to that time. Then ask:

• In one hour what time will it be? Ask students to set the new time on their clocks and talk with their partner about what time it will be and how they know. Ask them to describe what happens to the big hand and the small hand. Then ask them how that time will look on a digital clock (10:45).

• If it is 4:45 now, in one half hour what time will it be? Repeat using hour intervals beginning on the three-quarter hour (1:45, 3:45). Students set their clocks and record the new time (5:15). They describe the movement and position of the hands of the clock. Repeat using two more half hour intervals.

ACTIVITY

1 Introducing How Far Can You Jump?

10 MIN   CLASS

Show students the areas and starting lines you have set up for this activity and the materials they will be using.

To do this activity, you and your partner will take turns jumping from the starting line on the floor and measuring the length of that jump using adding machine tape. You will then measure the adding machine tape with something like craft sticks or your feet or paper clips to determine the length of your jump. You each make three different jumps: a frog jump, a rabbit jump, and a kid jump.

Explain the rules for each jump. ❶

Point out to students that they will jump by placing their toes up to the starting line. The length of the jump is measured from the front of the starting line to the back of the heel. ❷

Students jump in different ways. Then they work together to measure their jumps.

Each time you jump, mark your stopping point at your heel. Your partner will help you cut a strip of adding machine tape the same length as your jump. What are some ways to mark where your jump ends?

Teaching Notes

❶ **Different Jumps** The three jumps are designed so that when students compare the lengths of their jumps, they will be different lengths. **Frog Jump:** Jump from a squatting position, starting and ending with both hands and feet on the floor. **Rabbit Jump:** Jump from almost a standing position, with knees bent, feet together, and hands staying in the front. **Kid Jump:** Similar to a Rabbit Jump, except arms are used to pump forward.

❷ **Adjusting the Task** If a student in your class cannot jump, he or she can be the official referee, making sure that toes do not creep over the starting line and having the final say over disputes about length of jumps. Or, ask the student to decide how he or she wants to jump and how the jump should be measured.

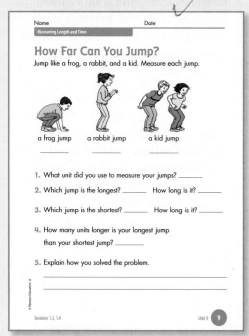

▲ **Student Activity Book, p. 9**

Students might suggest having a partner put a small object on the spot where they land, or marking their end points with masking tape. Have two students demonstrate how to cut the adding machine tape to show the length of the jump. One student jumps and marks where the jump ended. Then the partner tapes one end of the adding machine tape on the starting point, unrolls it to the endpoint, and cuts it. Suggest that students write on the adding machine tape to indicate their name and the jump that it represents (e.g., Rabbit Jump—Leo).

When you have finished your three jumps, choose your longest and shortest paper strips, which are your longest and shortest jumps. Choose one unit to measure those strips and record the lengths on *Student Activity Book* page 9. You can use craft sticks, yellow strips, blue strips, or foot lengths to measure.❸

Show the class how to measure with foot lengths, counting the number of heel-to-toe steps it takes to measure the length.

MATH WORKSHOP

② Measuring with Different Units

35 MIN

Students should finish Scavenger Hunt 2 in preparation for the discussion at the end of this session. Then they can begin How Far Can You Jump?

2A Scavenger Hunt 2: Blue and Yellow Strips

PAIRS

For complete details about this activity, see Session 1.2, page 30.

2B How Far Can You Jump?

PAIRS

Students take several jumps, and then cut pieces of adding machine tape to match the length of each jump. They compare their longest and shortest jumps by measuring the tapes with units they choose.❹

Students cut a piece of adding machine tape the same length as one of their jumps.

Teaching Note

❹ **Save the Paper Strips** Students must save the paper strips that measure their longest and shortest jumps for Sessions 1.4 and 1.5.

Professional Development

❺ **Teacher Note:** Measuring and Comparing: How Far Can You Jump?, p. 149

ONGOING ASSESSMENT: Observing Students at Work ✓

Students measure and compare the lengths of their different types of jumps.

- **How do students measure their jumps?** Do they lay out units one by one, counting by 1s as they go? Or, do they use groups of 10 (or 5) to count the units?

- **Do they iterate a single (or two) unit(s) which they lay down repeatedly, marking the end with their finger and keeping track of the units as they go?**

- **Are students accurate in their measurements?**

- **How do students find the difference between their longest and shortest jumps?** Do students directly compare the lengths for the two jumps and simply count how many units longer one is than the other? Do they count up from the smaller number to the larger? Do they subtract the smaller number from the larger?

- **Are students accurate in finding the difference between their longest and shortest jumps?**

As students measure their jumps, observe their measurement techniques. When they find the difference between their longest and shortest jumps, observe their strategies.❺

DIFFERENTIATION: Supporting the Range of Learners

Intervention If students are measuring by laying out multiple units, suggest that they try to use one or two of their selected units and work on iterating them.

Intervention If students are having difficulty getting an accurate measurement, observe to see whether they are not counting accurately or whether they are leaving gaps between units.

DISCUSSION

③ Measuring Accurately

15 MIN   CLASS

Math Focus Points for Discussion

◆ Estimating and calculating length using units that are related by a 2:1 ratio

◆ Identifying strategies for accurate measurement

◆ Considering sources for measurement error

Focus the first part of this discussion on the relationship between the blue and yellow strips in Scavenger Hunt 2.

I'm interested in how you estimated or figured out how many yellow strips long things were. When you found something that was four blue strips long, how did you estimate how many yellow strips long it would be? What did you notice about the blue and yellow strips that helped you?

Some students may have discovered that for each object, the number of yellow strips is twice the number of blue strips. Ask them why this is so.

Students might say:

"It's a pattern. You look at the blues you have and go 2, 4, 6, 8."

"It's doubles."

To encourage them to think about why the pattern works, line up one yellow strip next to a blue strip so that students can visualize how a second yellow strip would fit. Have a student place a second yellow strip next to the first one so that others can see that two yellow strips are equal in length to one blue strip. Ask students to describe this relationship.

Focus the second part of this discussion on students' measuring techniques.

Ask students to explain how they measured with the strips. Discrepancies in measurements may come up during this discussion. If so, you might use this as an opportunity to compare ways of measuring. Or you might offer your own example for discussion:

I noticed that some students measured the longest part of this [book] and found that it was four yellow strips long. When another student measured the same part of the [book], he used three yellow strips and part of another one. Do you think this [book] could have two different measurements?

Talk about some different ways these students might have measured, for example, lining up strips end-to-end versus leaving gaps between strips when lining them up. Do students see that one method is more accurate than another? Or, did one student round up to a whole number of strips (4 strips), while another student estimated the amount of the partial strip ($3\frac{1}{2}$ strips)?

Next ask students to share some of the ways they measured items that were more than five blue strips long.

You have only five blue strips in your set. How did you measure when you had to find something that was 10 strips long?

Students might have used the following strategies:

- Removing strips used in the beginning of the measuring and reusing them

- Flipping a strip over its end

- Using one unit over and over again by repeatedly marking where it ends and then placing it at that point

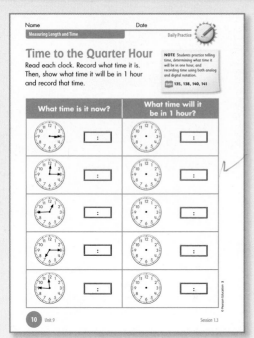

▲ Student Activity Book, p. 10

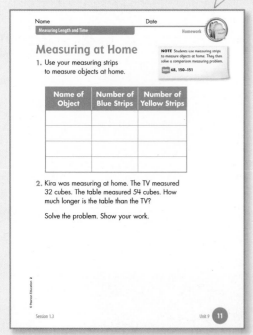

▲ Student Activity Book, p. 11

All of these strategies require iterating a unit and keeping track of how many times a unit is used, as compared to laying several units end-to-end and counting. Students will continue working to understand this more complex measurement technique.

SESSION FOLLOW-UP

Daily Practice and Homework

 Daily Practice: For ongoing review, have students complete *Student Activity Book* page 10.

 Homework: Students use the blue and yellow measuring strips from the previous homework, Measuring Strips (M4) to measure familiar objects at home. They record their work on *Student Activity Book* page 11. Have a few extra copies of Measuring Strips (M4) available for students who may need another copy.

 Student Math Handbook: Students and families may use *Student Math Handbook* pages 147, 148 for reference and review. See pages 172–178 in the back of this unit.

Measuring Jumps

Math Focus Points

◆ Iterating units to measure length

◆ Understanding that different-sized units yield different counts (the smaller the unit, the higher the count)

◆ Establishing the need for a common unit in order to compare measurements

Today's Plan		Materials
① MATH WORKSHOP **Jumping and Measuring** **①A How Far Can You Jump?** **①B How Many Blue Strips? How Many Yellow Strips?**	🕐 40 MIN	**①A** • Materials from Session 1.3, p. 36; blue and yellow measuring strips (from Session 1.2) **①B** • *Student Activity Book*, p. 13 • Blue and yellow measuring strips (from Session 1.2)
② DISCUSSION **Comparing Measurements**	🕐 20 MIN 👥 CLASS	• Chart: "Longest Jump/Shortest Jump"*
③ SESSION FOLLOW-UP **Daily Practice**		• *Student Activity Book*, p. 14 • *Student Math Handbook*, pp. 147, 150–151, 152

*See *Materials to Prepare*, p. 23.

Classroom Routines

Quick Images: Tens and Ones Show Image D, the 100 array, from *Quick Images 2: Tens and Ones* (T83). Follow the basic *Quick Images* activity. Students determine the total number of squares and share their strategies. Be sure to discuss the 10 × 10 structure of the array and the total number of squares (100). Repeat with Image E. Record equations to represent the image, such as 10 + 10 + 10 + 10 + 10 + 10 = 60. If no one mentions 100 − 40 = 60, ask students how they could use subtraction to determine the number of filled-in squares. Repeat with Image F.

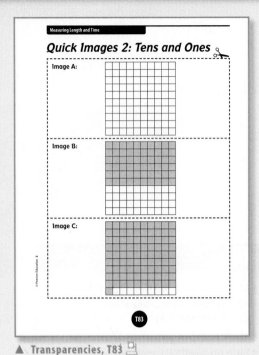

Measuring Length and Time

Quick Images 2: Tens and Ones ✂

Image A:

Image B:

Image C:

T83

▲ Transparencies, T83

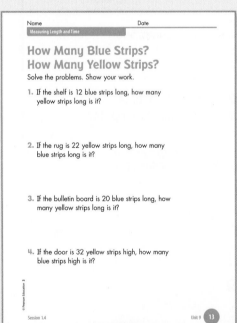

Name _____ Date _____

Measuring Length and Time

**How Many Blue Strips?
How Many Yellow Strips?**

Solve the problems. Show your work.

1. If the shelf is 12 blue strips long, how many yellow strips long is it?

2. If the rug is 22 yellow strips long, how many blue strips long is it?

3. If the bulletin board is 20 blue strips long, how many yellow strips long is it?

4. If the door is 32 yellow strips high, how many blue strips high is it?

Session 1.4   Unit 9 13

▲ Student Activity Book, p. 13

---

① Jumping and Measuring

40 MIN

Students finish measuring their jumps and record the results on *Student Activity Book* page 9. At the end of the session, students will discuss this work. If they finish measuring their jumps and find the difference between the shortest and longest, they can work on *Student Activity Book* page 13, in which they practice the doubling and halving relationships discussed in the previous session.

1A How Far Can You Jump?

INDIVIDUALS   PAIRS

For complete details about this activity, see Session 1.3, page 37.

1B How Many Blue Strips? How Many Yellow Strips?

INDIVIDUALS   PAIRS

Students work individually or in pairs to practice doubling and halving by answering if/then questions on *Student Activity Book* page 13.

Students solve problems that involve doubling and halving.

ONGOING ASSESSMENT: Observing Students at Work

Students work with the double/half relationship as they solve word problems.

- **Are students able to answer the questions based on the relationship between the units?** Can they both double a number and divide a number in half?

- **Do students need to lay out the number of units involved, or can they imagine the situation?**

DIFFERENTIATION: Supporting the Range of Learners

Extension For students who complete *Student Activity Book* page 13, give them several if/then situations with an odd number of yellow strips. (For example, if a desk is 9 yellow strips wide, how many blue strips wide is it? If a table is 23 yellow strips wide, how many blue strips wide is it?)

DISCUSSION

20 MIN   CLASS

② Comparing Measurements

Math Focus Points for Discussion

◈ Understanding that different-sized units yield different counts (the smaller the unit, the higher the count)

◈ Establishing the need for a common unit in order to compare measurements

Post the chart titled "Longest Jump/Shortest Jump." Go around the class and have students tell you their data and record them on the chart. Remember to include the unit that the student used to measure. If students measured with foot lengths, record the unit as "[Nate] foot lengths" or "[Keena] foot lengths" so that students recognize that different students used different units.

Teaching Notes

❶ **The Meaning of a Unit** We use the term *common unit* to mean a unit that is agreed upon by the class. This is in contrast to *standard units*, those that are used by the larger society, such as inches, feet, meters, etc.

❷ **Save the Paper Strips** Make sure students have their names on the paper strips that show their longest and shortest jumps. Store the strips so students can measure them with cubes in the next session.

▲ **Student Activity Book, p. 14**

Longest Jump/Shortest Jump

NAME	LONGEST JUMP	SHORTEST JUMP
Darren	24 yellow strips	16 yellow strips
Nadia	10 blue strips	6 blue strips
Luis	14 craft sticks	8 craft sticks
Holly	7 Holly foot lengths	5 Holly foot lengths

You have all figured out how much longer your longest jump is than your shortest jump. Let's say we want to know whose jump is the longest jump and whose is the shortest jump. We see all these measurements that were taken. Can we tell whose jump was the longest and whose jump was the shortest?

In this discussion, students should come to see that comparing counts is not sufficient for comparing measurements unless the same unit has been used.❶

We see that for [Darren's] longest jump, his number is higher than anyone else's in the class. Does that mean that his jump was the longest? Why does [Darren] have the highest number?

Some students may see and be able to explain that when they use smaller units, they end up with higher counts. This inverse relationship between the count and the size of the unit may be difficult for other students to see.

If we wanted to compare our jumps accurately, what would we need to do?

Once it is agreed that, in order to compare jumps, everyone needs to use the same unit, tell them that in the next session they will all measure their strips again—this time using connecting cubes as the unit.❷

SESSION FOLLOW-UP
③ Daily Practice

 Daily Practice: For ongoing review, have students complete *Student Activity Book* page 14.

 Student Math Handbook: Students and families may use *Student Math Handbook* pages 147, 150–151, 152 for reference and review. See pages 172–178 in the back of this unit.

Comparing Jumps

Math Focus Points

◆ Understanding that different-sized units yield different counts (the smaller the unit, the higher the count)

◆ Establishing the need for a common unit in order to compare measurements

◆ Solving comparison problems by finding the difference between two measurements

Today's Plan		Materials
ACTIVITY **❶ Remeasuring Jumps**	40 MIN PAIRS	• *Student Activity Book*, p. 15 • Connecting cubes (class set); students' strips of jump lengths (from Session 1.3 and 1.4)
DISCUSSION **❷ Comparing Measurements 2**	20 MIN CLASS	• Chart: "Measuring Our Jumps with Cubes"*
SESSION FOLLOW-UP **❸ Daily Practice**		• *Student Activity Book,* p. 16 • *Student Math Handbook,* pp. 150–151, 152

*See *Materials to Prepare,* p. 23.

Classroom Routines

Today's Number: 26 Using Subtraction Individually students generate expressions for 26 using only subtraction and 2 numbers. Remind them of the work you did with patterns in the previous Today's Number and ask them to generate 3 to 4 related expressions. For example: 27 — 1   28 — 2   29 — 3   30 — 4, or 30 — 4   40 — 14   50 — 24. Collect a number of examples on the board and discuss one or two patterns as a whole class.

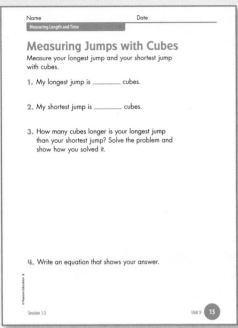

Name _____ Date _____

Measuring Length and Time

Measuring Jumps with Cubes

Measure your longest jump and your shortest jump with cubes.

1. My longest jump is _____ cubes.

2. My shortest jump is _____ cubes.

3. How many cubes longer is your longest jump than your shortest jump? Solve the problem and show how you solved it.

4. Write an equation that shows your answer.

Session 1.5   Unit 9 15

▲ **Student Activity Book, p. 15**

ACTIVITY

40 MIN   PAIRS

①Remeasuring Jumps

Explain that students will measure their longest and shortest jumps with connecting cubes, using the adding machine strips that match these jumps, and then they will find the difference between them. They will record this information on *Student Activity Book* page 15.

Students use a common unit to measure their jumps.

ONGOING ASSESSMENT: Observing Students at Work

Students measure their shortest and longest jumps using cubes and compare the two measurements.

- **How do students measure their jumps with connecting cubes?** Do they join cubes one by one, counting by 1s as they go or after all the cubes are laid out? Do they use groups of 10 (or 5) to count the cubes representing the distance? Do they use just 10 individual cubes, which they iterate to measure the distance?

- **How do students find the difference between their longest and shortest jumps?** Do they compare the cube towers for the two jumps and count how many cubes longer one is than the other? Do they add on from the smaller number to the larger? Do they subtract the smaller number from the larger number?

- **Are students able to record their work clearly and accurately so someone else can understand their strategy for finding the difference?**

As students work on this task, observe their measurement strategies as well as their calculation strategies.

DIFFERENTIATION: Supporting the Range of Learners

Intervention Some students may have recorded their measurements in half units and then have trouble finding the difference. In that case, have them round to the nearest whole number and then compute.

Intervention For students who are counting by 1s to find the length of and difference between jumps, suggest that they keep track of the number of cubes by marking every 10th cube with a piece of tape.

DISCUSSION

❷ Comparing Measurements 2

20 MIN   CLASS

Math Focus Points for Discussion

◆ Establishing the need for and using a common unit in order to compare measurements

As in the previous session, post the chart, "Measuring Our Jumps with Cubes," that you prepared for recording each student's longest and shortest jump. This time, students will discuss their revised measurements, recorded on *Student Activity Book* page 15. Go around the class and have students tell you their data and record them on the chart. Remember to include the unit "cubes" that the student used to measure.

Measuring Our Jumps with Cubes		
NAME	LONGEST JUMP	SHORTEST JUMP
Rochelle	85 cubes	50 cubes
Juan	75 cubes	62 cubes
Chen	88 cubes	58 cubes

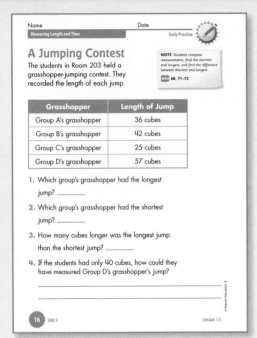

▲ **Student Activity Book, p. 16**

Now that students have all used a common unit, find the longest and the shortest jumps for the class. Record these on the board or another piece of chart paper for use in the next session. Ask the students to explain why they now can tell which jump is the longest (or shortest) when they could not tell in the earlier session.

As time allows, ask a few students to share their strategy for finding how much longer their longest jump is than their shortest jump.

In our next math session, we're going to compare the longest jump in the class to the shortest jump. Do you think that distance will be more than, less than, or about the same as the distance between your own jumps?

After a few students share their thoughts, tell them the class will return to this question in the next session.

SESSION FOLLOW-UP

③ Daily Practice

 Daily Practice: For reinforcement of this unit's content, have students complete *Student Activity Book* page 16.

 Student Math Handbook: Students and families may use *Student Math Handbook* pages 150–151, 152 for reference and review. See pages 172–178 in the back of this unit.

Assessment: A Measurement Disagreement

Math Focus Points

◆ Solving comparison problems by finding the difference between two measurements

◆ Considering sources of measurement error

Today's Plan		Materials
ACTIVITY **① Finding the Difference** 20 MIN INDIVIDUALS PAIRS		• *Student Activity Book*, p. 17 • Connecting cubes (class set); chart: "Measuring Our Jumps with Cubes"* (from Session 1.5)
DISCUSSION **② Strategies for Finding the Difference** 25 MIN CLASS		• Connecting cubes (optional)
ASSESSMENT ACTIVITY **③ A Measurement Disagreement** 15 MIN INDIVIDUALS		• M6*
SESSION FOLLOW-UP **④ Daily Practice**		• *Student Activity Book*, p. 18 • *Student Math Handbook*, pp. 148, 150–151 • M7–M8, Family Letter*

*See *Materials to Prepare,* p. 23.

Classroom Routines

What Time Is It?: What Time Will It Be? Write 1:45 on the board. Ask students to set their clocks to that time. Then ask:

• In one hour what time will it be?

Ask students to set the new time on their clocks and talk with their partner about what time it will be and how they know. Ask them to describe what happens to the big hand and the small hand. Then ask them how that time would look on a digital clock (2:45). Repeat using hour intervals beginning on the three-quarter hour (6:45, 10:45). Next, ask:

• If it is 11:45 now, in one half hour what time will it be?

Students set their clocks and record the new time (12:15). They describe the movement and position of the hands on the clock. Repeat using two more half hour intervals.

How Much Longer?

Use the information from your class to fill in the blanks.

1. The longest jump in the class was _____ cubes.

2. The shortest jump in the class was _____ cubes.

3. Write an equation.

How much longer was the longest jump than the shortest? Solve the problem.

Session 1.6 · Unit 9 · 17

▲ **Student Activity Book, p. 17** PORTFOLIO

ACTIVITY

① Finding the Difference

Students use *Student Activity Book* page 17 to record their thinking as they find the difference between the longest and shortest jumps in the class.

Yesterday we found the longest and shortest jumps in the class. [Jeffrey's] longest jump was [90] cubes, and that is the longest in the class. [Leo's] shortest jump was [25] cubes, and that is the shortest in the class. Today we're going to find how much longer the longest jump is than the shortest.

Students can work individually or in pairs. Encourage them to think about using an efficient strategy.

Students compare the lengths of two measurements.

ONGOING ASSESSMENT: Observing Students at Work

Students determine the difference between two measurements.

- **Do students directly compare measurements by laying out the number of cubes and counting the difference?** Do these students count by 1s or do they group cubes into 10s or 5s?

- **Do students represent the lengths on paper, using a diagram or a number line?**

- **Do students use an addition strategy such as counting or adding up from the smaller number to the larger?**

- **Do students subtract the smaller number from the larger?**

DIFFERENTIATION: Supporting the Range of Learners

Intervention Some students may benefit from building cube towers to represent the longest and shortest jumps. They can then compare the cube towers to find the difference.

DISCUSSION

2 Strategies for Finding the Difference

25 MIN **CLASS**

Math Focus Points for Discussion

◆ Solving a comparison problem by finding the difference between two measurements

Ask students for an equation that represents the difference between the longest and shortest jumps. Students might suggest any or all of the following, based on jumps of 25 and 90 cubes.

$$25 + 65 = 90$$

$$90 - 65 = 25$$

$$90 - 25 = 65$$

If students do not bring up both addition and subtraction, offer an equation yourself and ask students if it could also work to represent the problem and solution. Point out to the class that some students solved the problem by adding and others solved the problem by subtracting, and they all got the same answer.

Ask several students to share their strategies for finding the difference. Emphasize the efficiency of using groups of 10 (or other numbers).

ASSESSMENT ACTIVITY

3 A Measurement Disagreement

15 MIN **INDIVIDUALS**

Tell students that you are interested in seeing how they are thinking about the measurement that they have done so far. ❶ Give each student a copy of Assessment: A Measurement Disagreement (M6) and then read the problem aloud.

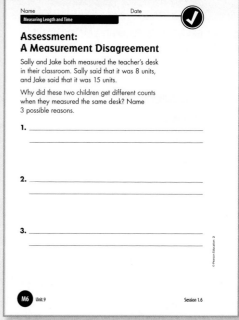

Name _____ Date _____

Measuring Length and Time

Assessment:
A Measurement Disagreement

Sally and Jake both measured the teacher's desk in their classroom. Sally said that it was 8 units, and Jake said that it was 15 units.

Why did these two children get different counts when they measured the same desk? Name 3 possible reasons.

1. _____
   _____

2. _____
   _____

3. _____
   _____

M6 Unit 9   Session 1.6

▲ Resource Masters, M6 **PORTFOLIO**

Teaching Note

❶ **Assessment** For this assessment, students are told about two children who measure an object and come up with different counts. They are asked to name three reasons why this may have happened. This problem assesses Benchmark 1 and Benchmark 3, and will provide a sense of what each student understands about the factors that must be taken into account when measuring an object.

Professional Development

2 **Teacher Note:** Assessment: A Measurement Disagreement, p. 150

Name _____ Date _____
Measuring Length and Time   Daily Practice

Today's Number: 25
Circle all of the problems that equal
Today's Number.

NOTE Students determine
if different expressions of
numbers are equal to 25.
Skill 55

Today's Number is 25.

$50 - 20 - 5$	$10 + 5 + 10 + 5$
$6 + 4 + 7 + 3 + 4 + 1$	$75 - 55$
$8 + 6 + 2 + 5 + 4$	$100 - 10 - 10 - 50 - 5$
$85 - 60 - 5$	$7 + 7 + 6 + 3 + 2$
$35 - 15$	$100 - 25 - 25 - 25$

18   Unit 9   Session 1.6

▲ **Student Activity Book, p. 18**

Differentiation

3 **English Language Learners** Check with English Language Learners to make sure they understand what they are being asked to do in this assessment. Some students may need support putting their ideas into writing. Consider providing a template to help them get started. For example: *Sally and Jake got different counts when they measured the desk because:*

1. _____

2. _____

3. _____

It may be possible in some classrooms to give English Language Learners who need it the option of writing in their native language. Another option may be to have them draw diagrams or pictures. You can also ask guided questions to help students, who are not yet able to write in English, explain their thinking while you jot down their responses.

Sally and Jake both measured the teacher's desk in their classroom. Sally said that it was 8 units, and Jake said that it was 15 units. Why did these two children get different counts when they measured the same desk? Name three possible reasons.

Students might consider a variety of factors:

• Measured different dimensions of the same object;

• Used different units of measure;

• Miscounted their units;

• Placed their units incorrectly.

ONGOING ASSESSMENT: Observing Students at Work

Students write about what might account for different measurements of the same object.

• **Do students' reasons cover a variety of measurement issues: the size of units, the object being measured, the placement of units, the counts?** **2** **3**

DIFFERENTIATION: Supporting the Range of Learners

Intervention If some students are confused by the word *unit,* have them name the different units they have been using.

SESSION FOLLOW-UP
4 Daily Practice

Daily Practice: For ongoing review, have students complete *Student Activity Book* page 18.

Student Math Handbook: Students and families may use *Student Math Handbook* page 148, 150–151 for reference and review. See pages 172–178 in the back of this unit.

Family Letter: Send home copies of the Family Letter (M7–M8).

INVESTIGATION 2

Mathematical Emphases

Linear Measurement Understanding length

Math Focus Points

◆ Identifying length and width as different dimensions of an object

Linear Measurement Using linear units

Math Focus Points

◆ Identifying strategies for accurate measurement

◆ Identifying and labeling partial units

Linear Measurement Measuring with standard units

Math Focus Points

◆ Creating and using a 12-inch measuring tool

◆ Iterating a 12-inch measuring tool

◆ Measuring lengths that are longer than 12 inches

Creating a Measuring Tool

	Student Activity Book	Student Math Handbook	Professional Development: Read Ahead of Time	
SESSION 2.1 p. 58				
The Land of Inch In the context of a fantasy story, students confront the need to measure objects with a common unit. They address the difficulty of aligning their units by creating a 12-inch measuring tool. They discuss strategies for using the tool.	19–20	146, 148, 149, 152, 155	• **Dialogue Box:** The Need for Measuring Tools, p. 168	
SESSION 2.2 p. 65				
Measuring with the Inch-Brick Tool The class reviews "measuring tips" from the previous session's discussion. During Math Workshop, students continue measuring objects with the inch-brick measuring tool.	19, 21–28	148, 155, 156	• **Teacher Note:** Cubes, Tiles, and Inch-Bricks, p. 153 • **Dialogue Box:** Measuring Lengths Longer Than 24 Inches, p. 169	
SESSION 2.3 p. 70				
A Map of the Land of Inch The class discusses how to use the inch-brick measuring tool to measure lengths longer than 12 inches. They make a map of the Land of Inch, marking off lengths that are longer than 12 inches.	23–24, 29–30	155, 156		

Classroom Routines See page 16 for an overview.

Quick Images

- T84, *Quick Images: Tens and Ones* 🖥 Cut apart the images on the transparency.

What Time Is It?

- Student clocks (1 per pair)
- Demonstration clock

Today's Number

- No materials needed

Materials to Gather	Materials to Prepare
• **Scissors** (1 per student) • **Envelopes** (1 per student) • **Card stock** (as needed) • **Craft stick** (1 per student) • **Glue stick** (1 per student)	• **M10, Inch-Bricks** Make copies on card stock. Cut into strips of 18 bricks. Place one strip in each envelope. (1 per student) • **M11, Measuring Tool Template** Make copies on card stock. Cut out the template. (1 per student) • **Demonstration measuring tool** Glue 12 Inch-bricks from M10 onto a Measuring Tool Template (M11). Number the units 1–12. • **Chart paper** Label the chart paper "Measuring Tips."
• **Chart: "Measuring Tips"** (from Session 2.1) • **Inch-brick measuring tool** (1 per student; from Session 2.1) • **Connecting cubes** (9 per student) • **Craft sticks** (2 per student) • **Color tiles** (8 per student) • **Markers** (as needed) • **Envelope with 6 inch-bricks** (1 per student; from Session 2.1)	• **Items to measure** Select a table, desk, chair, door, and bookcase to measure.
• **Inch-brick measuring tool** (1 per student; from Session 2.1) • **Chart: "Measuring Tips"** (from Session 2.1) • **Chart paper** (1 sheet per group) • **Glue stick** (1 per group) • **Scissors** (1 per group)	• **M12, Paths in the Land of Inch** Make copies. (1 per group)

🖥 Overhead Transparency

The Land of Inch

Math Focus Points

◆ Identifying length and width as different dimensions of an object

◆ Creating and using a 12-inch measuring tool

◆ Identifying strategies for accurate measurement

◆ Identifying and labeling partial units

Vocabulary

inch
measurement

Today's Plan

			Materials
①	**DISCUSSION** **The Land of Inch**	20 MIN · CLASS	• *Student Activity Book*, p. 19 • M10* • Scissors; envelopes; card stock; chart: "Measuring Tips"*
②	**ACTIVITY** **Creating a 12-inch Measuring Tool**	20 MIN · INDIVIDUALS	• *Student Activity Book*, p. 19 • M11* • Craft stick; glue stick; card stock; inch-bricks and envelopes (from Activity 1)
③	**DISCUSSION** **Using the Measuring Tool**	20 MIN · CLASS	• *Student Activity Book*, p. 19 • Inch-brick measuring tool (from Activity 2); chart: "Measuring Tips"
④	**SESSION FOLLOW-UP** **Daily Practice**		• *Student Activity Book*, p. 20 • *Student Math Handbook*, pp. 146, 148, 149, 152, 155

*See *Materials to Prepare*, p. 57.

Classroom Routines

Quick Images: Tens and Ones Show Image G from *Quick Images 3: Tens and Ones* (T83). Follow the basic *Quick Images* activity. Students determine the total number of shaded squares and share their strategies. Record equations to represent the image, such as $10 + 10 + 10 + 10 + 10 + 10 + 10 = 70$. If no one mentions $100 - 30 = 70$, ask students how they could use subtraction to determine the number of shaded squares. Repeat for Images H and I.

DISCUSSION

1 The Land of Inch

20 MIN   CLASS

Math Focus Points for Discussion

◆ Identifying length and width as different dimensions of an object

Introduce the story, Measuring in the Land of Inch, by relating it to the students' measuring experiences in this unit.❶

Here's a story about a kingdom where there was a contest to see who could jump the farthest. Listen to find out what happened when the athletes measured their jumps with different units.

Measuring in the Land of Inch.❷

Once upon a time, in a kingdom far, far away, there lived a miniature king whose miniature servants made his clothes, built his castle, paved the roads, and designed the gardens. They lived in the Land of Inch. One day, they were having a contest to see which of the athletes in the kingdom could jump the farthest. They ran into the same problem we did. At first, they measured their jumps with different units, so they couldn't tell who jumped the farthest. The king's favorite daughter, Princess Funer, came up with an idea when she saw a pile of bricks next to the castle that was being built for her. She said each athlete should measure her or his jump with bricks. The athletes all jumped again, measured their jumps with bricks, and they determined that Hap jumped the farthest. The king declared, "From now on, we will measure whatever we need to measure with bricks!"

The bricks were very heavy, and people got tired of carrying around so many. So Princess Funer had another idea. She cut pieces of paper the size of the bricks and said, "Since we live in the Land of Inch, and these pieces of paper are the same size as bricks, we'll call them *inch-bricks*." And the king declared, "From now on, we will measure whatever we need to measure with inch-bricks!"

Princess Funer gave inch-bricks to the people of the kingdom and now they use inch-bricks to measure everything.

Distribute envelopes each containing one strip of 18 Inch-Bricks ($1'' \times \frac{1}{2}''$ rectangles) from Inch-Bricks (M10).

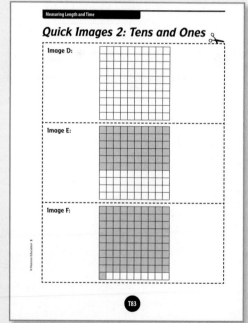

▲ Transparencies, T83

Teaching Note

❸ Measuring with Inch-Bricks Expect, that with these small pieces of paper, students will have difficulty placing the inch-bricks so that they are lined up without gaps or overlaps. This is, in fact, a difficulty we want them to encounter.

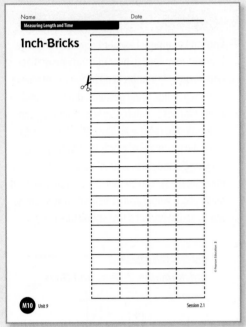

▲ **Resource Masters, M10**

Take a look at what is inside the envelope. These are inch-bricks, the same ones used to measure in the Land of Inch. First, you'll need to cut them along the lines so you can use the inch-bricks to measure.

A student cuts the inch-bricks apart.

Once students have cut their inch-bricks, introduce how they will be used.

Now we're going to use inch-bricks to see how far the different athletes in the Land of Inch could jump. For example, on *Student Activity Book* page 19 Pim jumped the width of the paper. What does the *width* of the paper mean?

Ask a couple of students to explain what is meant by *width*. Show students several examples of width, using the word *wide* as part of your explanation. In doing so, it is likely that you will also talk about the *length* of the paper or how *long* something is.

How can you use inch-bricks to figure out how far Pim jumped if he jumped the width of the paper?

Have students explain how they will use inch-bricks to figure out how far Pim jumped.

❷ ACTIVITY

Creating a 12-inch Measuring Tool
20 MIN INDIVIDUALS

Students begin to work on *Student Activity Book* page 19. Once most of the students have measured Pim's and Ren's jumps, call the class together to discuss any problems any student may be having measuring with the inch-bricks.❸ Students are likely to say that the inch-bricks keep moving around.

Collect students' measurements for Pim's jumps. Most likely, students will have different counts—between 7 and 10. Point out to students that they were measuring the same length, using the same units. Have them explain why they got different measurements.❹

Tell students that people in the Land of Inch had the same problem. Continue with the story.

In the Land of Inch, people could measure with the bricks, but the bricks were too heavy to carry. Inch-bricks, made of paper, were much easier to carry, but when people tried to lay them out, they had the same problem you're having; it was hard to keep the inch-bricks in place. Princess Funer had another idea. She said that the inch-bricks could be pasted down on a long piece of paper so that they wouldn't slide around. She called this the *inch-brick measuring tool*. Whenever they had to measure an item, the people from the Land of Inch could pull out their inch-brick measuring tool, hold it up against what needed to be measured, and count how many inch-bricks long it was.

Distribute the measuring tool template prepared from Measuring Tool Template (M11). (The template is 12 inches long, with spaces for 12 inch-bricks.) Show the class how to paste inch-bricks onto the template. Emphasize the need to line up the bricks end to end without gaps. When the measuring tool is complete, students return the extra 6 inch-bricks to their envelope. Collect the envelopes as they will be used in the next session.

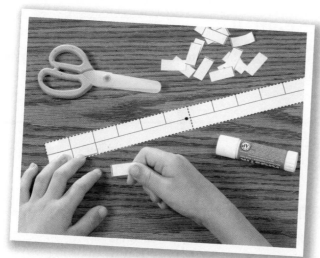

Students make their own 12-inch measuring tool by pasting inch-bricks onto the template.

Professional Development

❹ **Dialogue Box:** The Need for Measuring Tools, p. 168

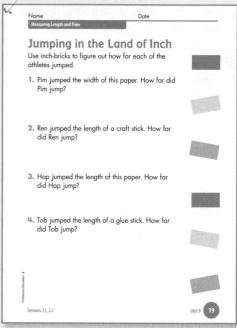

▲ **Student Activity Book, p. 19**

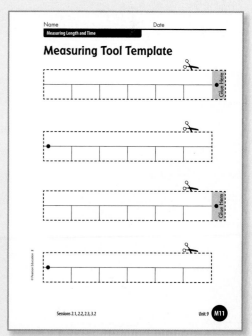

▲ **Resource Masters, M11**

Teaching Note

5 Measurement Discrepancy Pim jumped the width of a sheet of paper, which is $8\frac{1}{2}$ inches. Some students may have rounded their measurements to a whole number while others may have used fractions, thus there will be a discrepancy in their answers. Point out that "a little more than 8 inches," "a little less than 9 inches," and "$8\frac{1}{2}$ inches" are all ways of describing the same length.

Using their inch-brick measuring tool, students return to their work on *Student Activity Book* page 19. Have them check their measurements of Pim's and Ren's jumps. If they got different measurements using their tool, they should write the corrected measurement. Then they can answer any remaining questions.

ONGOING ASSESSMENT: Observing Students at Work

Students use their inch-brick tool to measure objects shorter than 12 inches.

- **How do students place their inch-bricks to measure?** Do they line them up end-to-end, without gaps or overlaps? (If they are physically unable to do this, is it their intention?)

- **Can students describe the difficulty of using individual inch-bricks and explain why different students got different measurements for the same object?**

- **How do students use the measuring tool?** Do they place the tool alongside the object to be measured and count the number of inch-bricks along the length of the object? Do students place the end of the measuring tool at the end of the object and count inch-bricks from the end of the tool?

- **Do any students number the units on their measuring tool?**

DIFFERENTIATION: Supporting the Range of Learners

Intervention Some students may need help pasting their inch-bricks on the template.

DISCUSSION

3 Using the Measuring Tool

20 MIN   CLASS

Math Focus Points for Discussion

◆ Identifying and labeling partial units

◆ Identifying strategies for accurate measurement

Ask students to share their measurements for Pim's, Ren's, Hap's, and Tob's jumps and record their responses. **5** Remind students of the work they did in the fractions unit and review the symbol used for $\frac{1}{2}$ inch.

Some students may mistakenly identify the width of the paper as $9\frac{1}{2}$ inches. That is, they may have included the partial unit in the whole-number count to get 9, and then recognizing that it was a partial unit, added $\frac{1}{2}$ for $9\frac{1}{2}$. In this case, ask the students how many *whole* inches fit across the width of the paper. Emphasize that $8\frac{1}{2}$ inches indicates 8 *whole* inches plus another $\frac{1}{2}$ inch.❻

Even with the issue of partial units resolved, discrepancies may arise. If so, take advantage of the opportunity they provide for talking about the strategies students used. Different results may be due to errors in using the measuring tool, such as not correctly lining up the tool along what is to be measured, or miscounting the number of units. Continue the discussion of strategies for accurate measurement.

Whenever we measure, there are a lot of things that we need to remember so that our measurements are accurate. Let's see whether we can make a list of those things.

Ask students to identify what they need to keep in mind in order to measure accurately and record them on the "Measuring Tips" chart you have prepared. Students are likely to share the following. If they do not, bring them up yourself:

- Start measuring from the beginning or one end of the object.
- Line up your measuring tool or unit.
- Count every unit on the tool.
- If you are using more than one unit or tool, lay them end to end; do not leave gaps.
- Measure in a straight line.
- Use a fraction to label part of a unit.

When we have a tool like the inch-brick measuring tool, there's something else we can do to make it easier to measure. We can number each of the inch-bricks.

Teaching Note

❻ **Partial Units** Students should be familiar with naming and labeling $\frac{1}{2}$ inches from their work in Unit 7, *Parts of a Whole, Parts of a Group*. Working with partial units is a difficult idea for some students to understand and they may need to revisit this conversation repeatedly.

Name _____ Date _____

Measuring Length and Time   Daily Practice

Addition Combinations and Sequencing Numbers

NOTE Students practice solving addition combinations and sequencing numbers from 1–100.

24, 43

1. Solve these problems. Fill in the totals on the 100 Chart below.

8 + 8 = _____   9 + 3 = _____   7 + 2 = _____

9 + 7 = _____   7 + 4 = _____   9 + 9 = _____

8 + 7 = _____   9 + 6 = _____   8 + 9 = _____

7 + 7 = _____   6 + 8 = _____   4 + 9 = _____

2. Fill in the other missing numbers on the 100 chart.

	2			6	7				
								19	
21			25	26					30
	33				37	39			
	42	44		46				49	50
	53		55						
61						68			
71		74		76				79	80
	82		85			88			
91	92	93			96				

20 Unit 9   Session 2.1

© Pearson Education 2

▲ **Student Activity Book, p. 20**

Point out to students that when you count inch-bricks on the tool, it is easy to lose track and count incorrectly. Show them your inch-brick tool with the units numbered from 1 to 12. Ask a student to show how to use your tool to measure an object. Have a few students demonstrate with different objects.

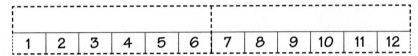

| 1 | 2 | 3 | 4 | 5 | 6 | 7 | 8 | 9 | 10 | 11 | 12 |

Have students number their inch-brick measuring tools. Then have students check with a partner to see that their tools are numbered the same.

SESSION FOLLOW-UP

4 Daily Practice

 Daily Practice: For ongoing review, have students complete *Student Activity Book* page 20.

 Student Math Handbook: Students and families may use *Student Math Handbook* pages 146, 148, 149, 152, 155 for reference and review. See pages 172–178 in the back of this unit.

Measuring with the Inch-Brick Tool

Math Focus Points

◆ Identifying strategies for accurate measurement

◆ Iterating a 12-inch measuring tool

◆ Measuring lengths that are longer than 12 inches

Vocabulary
accurately

Today's Plan		Materials
DISCUSSION **① Reviewing Measuring Tips** 15 MIN CLASS		• *Student Activity Book*, p. 19 (from Session 2.1) • Chart: "Measuring Tips"; students' inch-brick measuring tools (from Session 2.1)
MATH WORKSHOP **② Measuring with the Inch-Brick Tool** **②A** Clothes in the Land of Inch **②B** Buildings in the Land of Inch **②C** Children's Jumps in the Land of Inch 45 MIN		**②A** • *Student Activity Book*, pp. 21–22 • Students' inch-brick measuring tools; connecting cubes; craft sticks; color tiles **②B** • *Student Activity Book*, pp. 23–24 • Students' inch-brick measuring tools **②C** • *Student Activity Book*, pp. 25–26 • Students' inch-brick measuring tools; connecting cubes; markers; craft sticks; tiles
SESSION FOLLOW-UP **③ Daily Practice and Homework**		• *Student Activity Book*, pp. 27–28 • *Student Math Handbook*, pp. 148, 155, 156 • Envelope with 6 Inch-bricks (from Session 2.1)

Classroom Routines

Today's Number: 20 Using Subtraction Individually students generate expressions for 20 using subtraction and several numbers (e.g., 30 − 5 − 5, or 46 − 10 − 10 − 3 − 3). For each expression they write a corresponding expression using only two numbers (e.g., 30 − 5 − 5 = 30 − 10, or 46 − 10 − 10 − 3 − 3 = 46 − 26).

DISCUSSION

1 Reviewing Measuring Tips

15 MIN   CLASS

Math Focus Points for Discussion

◆ Identifying strategies for accurate measurement

For this discussion, take down the chart of "Measuring Tips" from the previous session. (You will put it up again in a few minutes.) Each student needs their measuring tool and a completed copy of *Student Activity Book* page 19.

Today you're going to have a lot of practice measuring different things in the Land of Inch. Before we get started, let's think about some of the measuring tips we listed in the last session to help us measure accurately.

Ask students whether they know what the word *accurately* means. If they do not, tell them that to *measure accurately* means, "to measure without errors."

What were some of the measuring tips that we put on our list? It's important to keep them in mind when we measure.

Once students have identified a few of the tips, post the chart on the board and ask students to read the tips silently. Discuss any tips that have not yet been mentioned today.

Students review their list of Measuring Tips.

As a way of revisiting how to measure partial units, have students re-measure Pim's jump, which was the width of the paper. Since the paper is $8\frac{1}{2}$ inches wide, the edge of the paper will be in the middle of the ninth inch-brick. Some students might think of this as $9\frac{1}{2}$. If there is disagreement, have students talk it through. Use the following questions to guide their thinking:

How many whole inch-bricks was Pim's jump?

What fractional part is added to the whole inch-bricks?

Is the width of the paper more than 9 inch-bricks or less?

MATH WORKSHOP

2 Measuring with the Inch-Brick Tool

45 MIN

In this Math Workshop, students practice measuring objects that are shorter and longer than their inch-brick measuring tool. Encourage students to label their measurements with the word *inches* or *inch-bricks*.

Most students are expected to complete Math Workshop Activities 1 and 2. The third activity is available for those who finish early. It poses comparison problems in which students find the difference between two lengths, some of which involve half-inches. Time is not allotted for discussion of these problems in the third activity. They are included for those students who need additional challenge.

2A Clothes in the Land of Inch

INDIVIDUALS

Students complete *Student Activity Book* pages 21–22.

ONGOING ASSESSMENT: Observing Students at Work

Students use their Inch-brick tool to measure objects shorter than 12 inches. ❶

- **How do students use the measuring tool?** Do they correctly align the end of the measuring tool with the end of the object?

- **Do students correctly read the number of units on the tool?** Are they able to determine the correct measurement when the length of an object is between two whole numbers?

DIFFERENTIATION: Supporting the Range of Learners

Intervention Some students may benefit from working with you in a small group and working through one or two of the measuring situations before they are confident about working independently.

Professional Development

❶ **Teacher Note:** Cubes, Tiles, and Inch-Bricks, p. 153

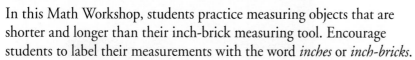

Name _____ Date _____
Measuring Length and Time

Clothes in the Land of Inch (page 1 of 2)

Measure each object with an inch-brick measuring tool. Record each length.

1. The length of Princess Funer's cloak is the same as the length of your pencil.

   How many inch-bricks is Princess Funer's cloak? _____

2. The length of Ren's jacket is the same as the length of 9 cubes.

   How many inch-bricks is Ren's jacket? _____

3. The length of Pim's shirtsleeve is the same as the length of 2 craft sticks.

   How many inch-bricks is Pim's shirt sleeve? _____

4. The length of Raf's knee sock is the same as the length of 4 cubes.

   How many inch-bricks is Raf's knee sock? _____

5. The length of Nim's pants is the same as the length of 4 color tiles.

   How many inch-bricks are Nim's pants? _____

Session 2.2   Unit 9   21

▲ **Student Activity Book, p. 21**

Name _____ Date _____
Measuring Length and Time

Clothes in the Land of Inch (page 2 of 2)

6. The height of the king's crown is the same as the length of 3 color tiles.

   How many inch-bricks high is the king's crown? _____

7. The length of Gar's jacket is the same as the length of 8 color tiles.

   How many inch-bricks is Gar's jacket? _____

Use the information above to solve each problem. Show your work.

8. How many more inch-bricks is Ren's jacket than Raf's knee sock?

9. How many more inch-bricks is Gar's jacket than the king's crown?

10. How many more inch-bricks are Nim's pants than the king's crown?

22   Unit 9   Session 2.2

▲ **Student Activity Book, p. 22**

Professional Development

② Dialogue Box: Measuring Lengths Longer Than 24 Inches, p. 169

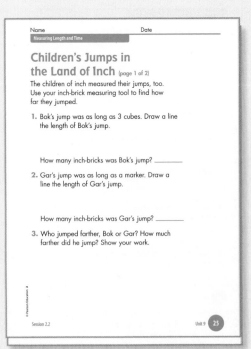

Name _____ Date _____
Measuring Length and Time

Buildings in the Land of Inch (page 1 of 2)
Use your inch-brick measuring tool to answer each question.

1. The people in the Land of Inch grow to be about as tall as the inch-brick measuring tool. How many inch-bricks tall are the people in the Land of Inch?

2. Princess Funer's castle is about as long as the table. How many inch-bricks long is Princess Funer's castle?

3. Tob's house is about as wide as your desk. How many inch-bricks wide is Tob's house?

Session 2.2   Unit 9   23

▲ **Student Activity Book, pp. 23–24**

Name _____ Date _____
Measuring Length and Time

Children's Jumps in the Land of Inch (page 1 of 2)
The children of inch measured their jumps, too. Use your inch-brick measuring tool to find how far they jumped.

1. Bok's jump was as long as 3 cubes. Draw a line the length of Bok's jump.

   How many inch-bricks was Bok's jump? _____

2. Gar's jump was as long as a marker. Draw a line the length of Gar's jump.

   How many inch-bricks was Gar's jump? _____

3. Who jumped farther, Bok or Gar? How much farther did he jump? Show your work.

Session 2.2   Unit 9   25

▲ **Student Activity Book, pp. 25–26**

Intervention Students who are still sorting out how to use the inch-brick measuring tool should stay with this activity. Find additional objects shorter than 12 inches for them to measure.

② ⓑ Buildings in the Land of Inch

PAIRS

Students complete *Student Activity Book* pages 23–24. Encourage them not to borrow measuring tools from another pair, but to measure using only the two inch-brick measuring tools they have.②

Students measure lengths longer than 24 inches with their inch-brick measuring tools.

ONGOING ASSESSMENT: Observing Students at Work

Students measure objects that are longer than their measuring tool.

- **When measuring objects between 12 and 24 inches, do students iterate one measuring tool or do they use two tools?**

- **How do students measure objects longer than 24 inches?**

- **How do students calculate the total number of Inch-bricks?** For example, if the height of the chair is 20 inch-bricks, do they see that they add 12 (from the first time they placed the measuring tool) and 8 (from the second time they placed the measuring tool)?

② ⓒ Children's Jumps in the Land of Inch

INDIVIDUALS

Students complete *Student Activity Book* pages 25–26. This activity poses problems about comparing different lengths (e.g., How much longer is Gar's jump than Bok's jump?). Have students work on this activity only if they can confidently and accurately measure objects that are shorter than and longer than 12 inches. Find time to discuss this work with those students who complete the activity.

ONGOING ASSESSMENT: Observing Students at Work

Students draw lines of given lengths and compare two different lengths.

- **How do students find the difference between two lengths?** Do they count on from the shorter length or count back from the longer? Do they use their measuring tool to count?

- **Can students use the tool to draw a line segment of specific length?**

You can use this activity as an additional check to determine whether students are able to use their measuring tool correctly. It also provides the challenge of finding the difference between two lengths that may be measured in half-inch-bricks. Use the above questions, along with the ones found on page 68 to guide your observations

DIFFERENTIATION: Supporting the Range of Learners

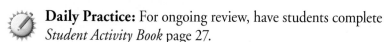 **Extension** These comparison problems with fractional units are included for students who need additional challenge.

SESSION FOLLOW-UP

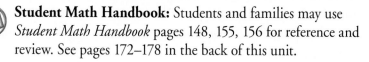

3 Daily Practice and Homework

Daily Practice: For ongoing review, have students complete *Student Activity Book* page 27.

Homework: Each student will need an envelope that contains 6 inch-bricks to use with *Student Activity Book* page 28. Explain to the students that they will use these inch-bricks to measure a variety of objects at home. If they choose, they can paste their inch-bricks onto the measuring tool at the bottom of the page.

Student Math Handbook: Students and families may use *Student Math Handbook* pages 148, 155, 156 for reference and review. See pages 172–178 in the back of this unit.

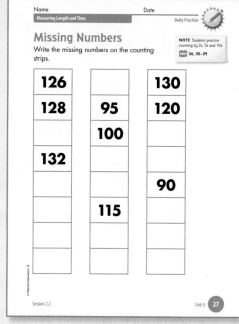

▲ Student Activity Book, p. 27

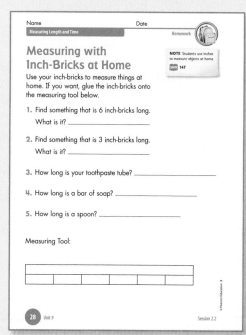

▲ Student Activity Book, p. 28

A Map of the Land of Inch

Math Focus Points

◆ Iterating a 12-inch measuring tool

◆ Measuring lengths that are longer than 12 inches

Today's Plan			Materials
DISCUSSION ① **Longer than 12 Inches**	15 MIN	CLASS	• *Student Activity Book*, pp. 23–24 (from Session 2.2) • Inch-brick measuring tool; (from Session 2.1); Chart: "Measuring Tips" (from Session 2.1)
ACTIVITY ② **Maps of the Land of Inch**	35 MIN	GROUPS	• *Student Activity Book*, p. 29 • M12* • Students' inch-brick measuring tools (from Session 2.1); chart paper; glue stick; scissors
DISCUSSION ③ **Sharing Maps**	10 MIN	CLASS	• Students' Land of Inch maps (from Activity 2); inch-brick measuring tool; (from Session 2.1)
SESSION FOLLOW-UP ④ **Daily Practice**			• *Student Activity Book*, p. 30 • *Student Math Handbook*, pp. 155, 156

*See *Materials to Prepare*, p. 57.

Classroom Routines

What Time Is It?: What Time Will It Be? Write 4:45 on the board. Ask students to set their clocks to that time. Then ask,

In one hour what time will it be?

Ask students to set the new time on their clocks and talk with their partner about what time it will be and how they know. Then ask them how that time will look on a digital clock (5:45). Repeat using hour intervals beginning on the three-quarter hour (2:45, 6:45). Next, ask,

If it is 3:45 now, in one half hour what time will it be?

Students set their clocks and record the new time (4:15). They describe the movement and position of the hands on the clock. Repeat using two more half-hour intervals.

DISCUSSION

15 MIN   CLASS

1 Longer than 12 Inches

Math Focus Points for Discussion

◆ Measuring lengths that are longer than 12 inches

Based on their work on *Student Activity Book* pages 23–24, students share their strategies for measuring objects that are longer than 12 inches. As they demonstrate their measuring techniques, highlight important strategies by commenting and questioning as they demonstrate. In particular, look for opportunities to discuss where students first place their measuring tool and strategies they use to mark the end of the first placement of the tool to know where to place it to continue measuring. Also discuss how they figured out the total number of Inch-bricks.

After the demonstrations, ask the class what to add to the "Measuring Tips" chart for measuring lengths longer than the measuring tool.

Students use a craft stick to mark the spot where the first placement of the tool ends.

Math Note

❶ A Different Task Measuring an object that is longer than 12 inches is a different task from marking off a length longer than 12 inches. Some students who successfully measured objects for *Student Activity Book* pages 23–24 may find this task challenging.

▲ **Resource Masters, M12**

ACTIVITY

2 Maps of the Land of Inch

35 MIN GROUPS

In this activity, students will practice measuring lengths greater than 12 inches by creating a map of the Land of Inch. Each group of three students is given a piece of chart paper, on which they will draw their map, and a copy of Paths in the Land of Inch (M12). They cut out pictures of the King's Castle, the King's Garden, Princess Funer's Castle, and Pim's House, and paste them onto the map according to the constraints given on *Student Activity Book* page 29. Specifically, the King's Castle is placed in a corner of the chart paper, and the other objects are particular distances away. For each object, students draw a straight-line path the length of the given distance from the King's Castle and paste the object at the other end of the path.❶ Students write the length of each path on the map.

As time allows, students can draw in other landmarks in the Land of Inch. For each item they draw, they also draw a path to the King's Castle (or to some other object on the map) and measure the length of that path.

ONGOING ASSESSMENT: Observing Students at Work

Students measure lengths that are longer than 12 inches.

- **When measuring lengths between 12 and 24 inches, do students iterate one measuring tool or do they use two tools?**

- **How do students measure lengths longer than 24 inches?**

- **How do students calculate the total number of inch-bricks?**
  For example, for a length of 15 inches, do they see that they add 12 (from the first placement of the measuring tool) and 3 (from the second placement)?

DIFFERENTIATION: Supporting the Range of Learners

Intervention If some students are still having difficulty with the basics of using the measuring tool, have them create a map with shorter lengths. Suggest that they place the King's Castle in the center of the page and the King's Garden, Princess Funer's Castle, and Pim's House in locations of their choice. Then they can draw in the paths and measure them.

Intervention If students do understand the basics of using the measuring tool, but have difficulty measuring lengths longer than 12 inches, do not simplify the task for them. Instead, discuss with them the points made in the discussion at the beginning of the session about different strategies for measuring objects longer than the tool.

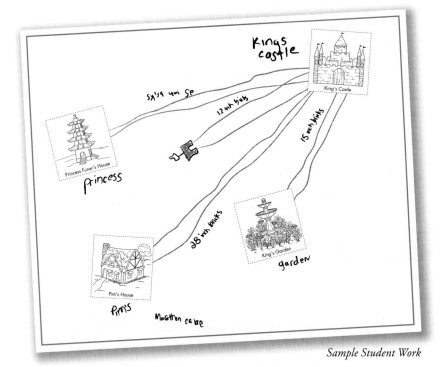

Sample Student Work

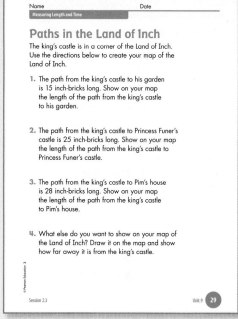

Name _____ Date _____
Measuring Length and Time

Paths in the Land of Inch

The king's castle is in a corner of the Land of Inch.
Use the directions below to create your map of the
Land of Inch.

1. The path from the king's castle to his garden
   is 15 inch-bricks long. Show on your map
   the length of the path from the king's castle
   to his garden.

2. The path from the king's castle to Princess Funer's
   castle is 25 inch-bricks long. Show on your map
   the length of the path from the king's castle to
   Princess Funer's castle.

3. The path from the king's castle to Pim's house
   is 28 inch-bricks long. Show on your map
   the length of the path from the king's castle
   to Pim's house.

4. What else do you want to show on your map of
   the Land of Inch? Draw it on the map and show
   how far away it is from the king's castle.

© Pearson Education 2

Session 2.3   Unit 9   29

▲ **Student Activity Book, p. 29**

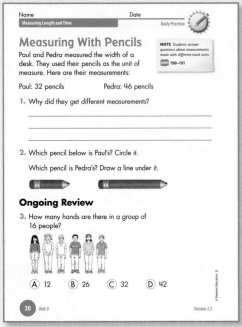

▲ **Student Activity Book, p. 30**

DISCUSSION

3 Sharing Maps

10 MIN   CLASS

Math Focus Points for Discussion

◆ Measuring lengths that are longer than 12 inches

Allow students to:

- Share their maps of the Land of Inch

- Discuss the problems they faced as they measured the paths

- Share the strategies they developed to measure lengths longer than 12 or 24 inches

SESSION FOLLOW-UP

4 Daily Practice

 Daily Practice: For reinforcement of this unit's content, have student complete *Student Activity Book* page 30.

 Student Math Handbook: Students and families may use *Student Math Handbook* pages 155, 156 for reference and review. See pages 172–178 in the back of this unit.

Mathematical Emphases

Linear Measurement Using linear units

Math Focus Points

◆ Recognizing that, given equal counts of two different units, the larger unit marks off a longer length

◆ Understanding that different-sized units yield different counts (the smaller the unit, the higher the count)

Linear Measurement Measuring with standard units

Math Focus Points

◆ Establishing the need for and using a standard unit of measure

◆ Using a ruler as a standard measuring tool

◆ Comparing a variety of measuring tools

◆ Becoming familiar with the terms *inches, feet, yards, centimeters,* and *meters* as standard units of measure

◆ Using inches, feet, yards, centimeters, and meters to describe lengths

◆ Measuring lengths that are longer than 12 inches

◆ Comparing centimeters and inches

This Investigation also focuses on

◆ Solving comparison problems by finding the difference between two measurements

Two Measurement Systems

	Student Activity Book	Student Math Handbook	Professional Development: Read Ahead of Time	
SESSION 3.1 p. 78				
Assessment: The King's Foot Students demonstrate their understanding of the importance of standard measures as they respond to a story about a king who has difficulty communicating building directions to a carpenter. They are introduced to rulers and yardsticks.	31	150–151, 152, 155	• **Teacher Note:** Learning to Measure Length, p. 147; Assessment: The King's Foot, p. 154	
SESSION 3.2 p. 85				
Rulers and Body Benchmarks Students explore how their inch-brick measuring tools compare with rulers and discuss what they find. In Math Workshop, students use rulers to measure familiar objects in the classroom and locate *benchmark measurements* on their bodies.	32–38	153, 155, 156	• **Teacher Note:** Learning to Use a Ruler, p. 157; Benchmarks on the Body, p. 156 • **Dialogue Box:** What's the Length and What's the Width?, p. 167	
SESSION 3.3 p. 91				
Measurement Strategies Students discuss strategies for how to measure objects that are longer than 1 foot. In Math Workshop, students use rulers to measure familiar objects in the classroom, locate benchmark measurements on their bodies that they can use to estimate lengths without a ruler, and measure the width (or length) of the classroom.	33–35, 39–42	153, 156–157	• **Dialogue Box:** Measuring Lengths Longer Than 24 Inches, p. 169	
SESSION 3.4 p. 96				
Moving to Metric Students are introduced to centimeters and meters as a different system of measurement used by most of the world. They begin to develop centimeter awareness by making their own centimeter and meter measures. In Math Workshop, they use these tools to identify objects that are about 1 meter and about 1 centimeter long, and compare the two sides of their rulers, one marked in inches and the other in centimeters.	43–46	154	• **Teacher Note:** Background on the Metric System, p. 158	
SESSION 3.5 p. 101				
Metric Measurement Students briefly discuss the results of their metric scavenger hunt and their comparisons of the two sides of their rulers. They measure a variety of objects in inches and in centimeters and discuss their results.	44, 46, 47–48	150–151, 153, 154, 155		

Classroom Routines
See page 16 for an overview.

How Many Pockets?	What Time Is It?
• **Class list** (1 per student)	• **Demonstration clock**
Quick Images	• **Student clocks** (1 per pair)
• **T85–T86, Cut apart the images.** *Quick Images 4 and 5:*	**Today's Number**
Tens and Ones 🖥	• **No materials needed**

Materials to Gather	Materials to Prepare
• **Rulers** (1 per pair) • *How Big Is a Foot?* **by Rolf Myller** (optional)	• **Starting line** Tape a 3-foot "starting line" to the floor at the front of the classroom, using masking or electrical tape. • **M13, Assessment: The King's Foot** Make copies. (1 per student)
• **Rulers** (1 per student) • **Yardstick** (1 or 2) • **Tape measure** (1 or 2) • **Inch-Brick measuring tool** (1 per student; from Session 2.1) • **Yellow strips and blue strips** (from Investigation 1)	• **Chart paper** Make a chart titled "Body Benchmarks" with 3 headings: "1 inch," "6 inches," and "12 inches (1 foot)."
• **Chart: "Body Benchmarks"** (from Session 3.2) • **Rulers** (1 per student) • **Yardsticks**	
• **World map or globe** (optional) • **Centimeter cubes** (as needed) • **Rulers** (1 per student) • **Scissors** (1 per student) • **Tape** • **Metersticks** (as needed)	• **M16, Centimeter Grid Paper** Make copies. (1 per student) • **Meter strip** Prepare a 3-centimeter-wide meter strip from Centimeter Grid Paper (M16). • **Chart paper** Prepare two charts, one with the heading "Things About 1 Centimeter Long in School," and the other headed "Things About 1 Meter Long in School."
• **Rulers** (1 per student) • **Pencil** (1 per student) • **Book** (1 per pair) • **Scissors** (1 per pair)	• **Chart paper:** Prepare two charts, one with the heading "Things About 1 Centimeter Long at Home," and the other headed "Things About 1 Meter Long at Home." • **Chart paper** Prepare a chart with 6 columns. Write three main headings with each covering 2 columns: "Pencil," "Book," and "Scissors." Label the two columns under each main heading as "Inches" and "Centimeters."

🖥 Overhead Transparency

Assessment: The King's Foot

Math Focus Points

- Establishing the need for and using a standard unit of measure
- Using a ruler as a standard measuring tool
- Recognizing that, given equal counts of two different units, the larger unit marks off a longer length

Vocabulary

unit
footlength
ruler

Today's Plan		Materials
DISCUSSION **① Measuring with Footlengths** 15 MIN · CLASS		• Masking tape starting line*
ASSESSMENT ACTIVITY **② The King's Foot** 25 MIN · INDIVIDUALS	✓	• M13* • *How Big Is a Foot?* by Rolf Myller (optional)
DISCUSSION **③ The Carpenter's Solution** 20 MIN · CLASS		• Rulers
SESSION FOLLOW-UP **④ Daily Practice**		• *Student Activity Book,* p. 31 • *Student Math Handbook,* pp. 150–151, 152, 155

*See *Materials to Prepare,* p. 77.

Classroom Routines

How Many Pockets?: Using a Class List to Add Distribute a class list to each student. Students record each other's pocket data on the class list as it is announced. Once all the data have been collected, students calculate the amount of money the pockets are worth. Some students calculate the total worth if each pocket is worth 1¢. Others calculate the total if each pocket is worth 5¢ or 10¢. Adjust the amount according to the level of each student. When groups of students are finished, have them compare their results with others who calculated the same coin amount.

DISCUSSION
Measuring with Footlengths

15 MIN   CLASS

Math Focus Points for Discussion

◆ Recognizing that, given equal counts of two different units, the larger unit marks off a longer length

Remind students that sometimes it is convenient to measure with footlengths as the unit.

When we were measuring how far you jumped, you used several different units. Some people used footlengths by stepping off the length heel-to-toe.

Ask one of your students to demonstrate.

We are going to use this piece of tape [point to the tape on the floor] as a starting line. Where should [Rochelle] place her foot to take the first step? Should her toe be on the line, or should her heel be on the line?

Have the class count 10 footlengths together as [Rochelle] marks them off. Mark the ending step with a piece of tape. This length is measured from the starting line to the front of the toe.

Now select another student, one with a different-sized foot.

[Malcolm] will take 10 steps, just like [Rochelle]. Do you think his 10 steps will be longer than, or shorter than, or the same length as [Rochelle's]?

A student uses footlengths to measure.

Teaching Notes

❶ **Act It Out** You may wish to have students act out the story as you read it aloud.

❷ **Making a Connection** Some students may ask whether this king and princess live in the Land of Inch. Wait to address this question until you hand out rulers in the next activity after reading the end of the story.

Have the second child take 10 heel-to-toe steps and again mark off where he ended.

Then ask students to compare that measure to the length of the first.

[Rochelle] and [Malcolm] both took 10 steps. Why did they measure off different lengths?

Some students will explain that since one person's foot was longer than the other person's foot, that person marked off a longer length.

ASSESSMENT ACTIVITY

25 MIN INDIVIDUALS

② The King's Foot

"The King's Foot" is a story about a king, a carpenter, a horse stall, and the importance of agreeing on a standard unit of measure. Read the story to your students.❶

Here's a story about a king who measured with heel-to-toe steps. Listen to find out how well it worked for him.

"The King's Foot"

Once upon a time there was a king who kept ponies. His daughter, the princess, had a pony of her own that she dearly loved.❷ As the princess grew older, she grew bigger but the pony did not. The day came when she climbed on her pony and her feet dragged on the ground. That was the day the king decided that he would surprise his daughter with a beautiful horse.

The king went to the best stable in the kingdom and chose a sleek Arabian mare. "Because it's a surprise," the king said, "I want to leave the mare here at your stable until I can get a new stall built in the royal barns to fit such a grand, large horse."

The king knew that he would have to tell the royal carpenter how large to make the stall. So, using heel-to-toe steps, the king carefully walked around the mare, imagining how big the stall for this beautiful horse should be.

". . . 5, 6, 7, 8, 9 feet long," he murmured, "and 3, 4, 5 feet wide. I will tell the royal carpenter to build a stall that is 9 feet long and 5 feet wide."

The king jotted down the numbers: 9 feet long and 5 feet wide. The message was sent to the carpenter, and she set to work at once. The first thing she did was to measure out the size of the stall. Using heel-to-toe steps, she measured 9 feet for the length and 5 feet for the width.

Soon the stall was ready and the king sent for the mare. He thought he would have a little fun with the princess, so he had the royal groom hide the mare behind the barn. Then he said to the princess, "Come with me and see if you can guess your surprise."

Together they walked into the royal barn, past all the stalls of the little ponies. They stopped in front of the empty new stall. But no sooner had the princess inspected the new stall then she burst into tears.

"I truly hoped that my surprise would be a horse, because I have outgrown my little pony. But now that I see the size of the stall, I know that you are just giving me another little pony, no larger than the first."

The king was puzzled. He saw that indeed, the new stall was much too small for a full-size horse. The groom quickly brought the new Arabian mare out of hiding, and as soon as the princess laid eyes on her, she forgot her tears. Only the king did not forget. He called angrily for the royal carpenter to account for her terrible mistake.

The carpenter was shocked. She knew she was good at her trade; her work always drew high praise. And she had made the stall just as the king had said—9 feet long and 5 feet wide, when she measured the size of the stall. What could have happened?

The story is asking us what could have happened. Why was the stall that the carpenter built too small for the horse? Before I finish reading the rest of the story, write a letter to the carpenter explaining what happened. Your letter should include an explanation of what went wrong, what she could do to correct the problem, and a diagram or picture to show why the stall was too small.

Teaching Notes

❸ A Different Story *How Big Is a Foot?* by Rolf Myller has a similar theme. In this book, the carpenter's apprentice gets thrown in jail because the bed he makes for the queen is too small. If you can get this book, you can substitute it for "The King's Foot." At the point in the book when the apprentice is thrown in jail and the story asks, "Why was the bed too small for the queen?," pause so that students can respond in writing to this question, composing a letter to the carpenter's apprentice.

❹ Assessment This assessment activity assesses students' understanding of the connection between the size of the unit and the size of the measure and the need to use a standard measure when measuring and communicating measurements. You will also be able to evaluate students' use of diagrams to illustrate a problem or a proposed solution to a problem. This assessment addresses Benchmark 2: Recognize that the same count of different-sized units yields different lengths.

Professional Development

❺ Teacher Note: Learning to Measure Length, p. 147; Assessment: The King's Foot, p. 154

Name _____ Date _____
Measuring Length and Time

Assessment: The King's Foot

The carpenter made a new stall for the king, but it was too small to fit the new horse for the princess. Write a letter to the carpenter. Your letter should answer these questions:

Why was the stall too small for the horse?

What could the carpenter do to correct her mistake?

_____
_____
_____
_____
_____
_____
_____
_____
_____
_____
_____
_____

Also, on the back of the paper, make a diagram or picture to show why the stall was too small.

Session 3.1   Unit 9 **M13**

▲ **Resource Masters, M13**

Students will probably need 15–20 minutes to compose their letters using Assessment: The King's Foot (M13). They should draw their picture or diagram on the back of the paper. (You will need to adapt this sheet if you are using the book, *How Big Is a Foot?*)❸ Remind them that they should respond with mathematical arguments—that is, they should explain *mathematically* why the stall was too small. Encourage them to be clear and specific about their ideas and suggestions.❹❺

ONGOING ASSESSMENT: Observing Students at Work

Students make mathematical arguments, including diagrams, to illustrate their reasoning about a measurement discrepancy.

- **Do students use a mathematical argument that makes sense?** Do they convey the idea that the carpenter's feet were smaller than the king's feet and thus the stall was smaller than the king intended?

- **Do students understand that the king and carpenter need to agree on a particular unit of measure?**

- **Do they use a diagram to help illustrate either the problem or the solution to the problem?**

DIFFERENTIATION: Supporting the Range of Learners

ELL If you are using the book *How Big Is a Foot?* be sure to show the pictures as you read it. If you are reading "The King's Foot" aloud, have students act out the story to help make it comprehensible to English Language Learners. It may be possible in some classrooms to give English Language Learners who need it the option of writing the letter in their native language. Other options include having them draw a diagram or picture that shows what the carpenter could do to correct the problem. In addition, with the help of guided questions from you, some students who may not yet be able to write in English with much fluency, may have adequate oral skills to explain what went wrong and what needs to be done to correct the problem.

DISCUSSION

③ The Carpenter's Solution

20 MIN   CLASS

Math Focus Points for Discussion

◆ Establishing the need for and using a standard unit of measure

◆ Recognizing that, given equal counts of two different units, the larger unit marks off a longer length

When students have finished their letters, collect their papers and take a few minutes to have them share their ideas with the class, and then finish reading the story.

"The King's Foot" (continued)

The carpenter stared sadly at her work. She paced thoughtfully around the little stall, carefully counting her footlengths. Then she sat down beside the king to think, staring at her feet.

That was when the carpenter noticed something—when she saw the king's foot next to hers. "That's it!" she cried. "Your foot is much longer than mine! I made the stall 9 feet long, but I used 9 of my feet instead of 9 of the king's feet."

Then the carpenter had a truly remarkable idea. She took a flat stick of wood, and she cut it exactly the same length as the king's foot. "This way," she told the king, "I can always know exactly how big you want me to build something."

Now the carpenter made a stall for the new horse that was 9 king's feet long and 5 king's feet wide. This time the stall was perfect. So the king was happy, and the princess was happy, and the carpenter was happiest of all.⑥ She started a factory and made lots of sticks just as long as the king's foot, which she called rulers. Selling these sticks, she became rich and famous.

Teaching Note

⑥ **Mathematical Reasoning** If students are still curious about whether the king and princess live in the Land of Inch, point out that the king's foot is the length of a ruler. Remind students that people in the Land of Inch grow to be about as tall as their inch-brick measuring tool, and the king's castle in the Land of Inch is about as high as the bookcase. Do they think it's the same king?

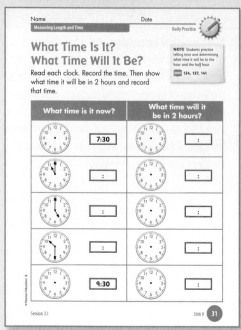

▲ **Student Activity Book, p. 31**

Distribute rulers to pairs of students so that they can see the "sticks" that the carpenter in the story made. Session 3.2 begins with a discussion about measuring tools.

SESSION FOLLOW-UP
4 Daily Practice

Daily Practice: For ongoing review, have students complete *Student Activity Book* page 31.

Student Math Handbook: Students and families may use *Student Math Handbook* pages 150–151, 152, 155 for reference and review. See pages 172–178 in the back of this unit.

Rulers and Body Benchmarks

Math Focus Points

◆ Comparing a variety of measuring tools

◆ Solving comparison problems by finding the difference between two measurements

◆ Becoming familiar with the terms *inches*, *feet,* and *yards* as standard units of measure

◆ Using a ruler as a standard measuring tool

<table>
<tr><th colspan="2">Vocabulary</th></tr>
<tr><td>tape measure</td><td>inch</td></tr>
<tr><td>yardstick</td><td>foot</td></tr>
<tr><td>yard</td><td>benchmark</td></tr>
</table>

Today's Plan		Materials
ACTIVITY ① **Inch-Bricks and Rulers**	20 MIN PAIRS	• *Student Activity Book,* p. 32 • Rulers; yardstick; tape measure; inch-brick measuring tool (from Investigation 2)
DISCUSSION ② **Comparing Tools**	15 MIN CLASS	• Yellow strips and blue strips (from Investigation 1)
MATH WORKSHOP ③ **Measuring** ③A **Body Benchmarks** ③B **Measure and Compare**	25 MIN	3A • *Student Activity Book,* p. 33 • Chart: "Body Benchmarks"*; rulers 3B • *Student Activity Book,* pp. 34–35 • Rulers
SESSION FOLLOW-UP ④ **Daily Practice and Homework**		• *Student Activity Book,* pp. 36–38 • *Student Math Handbook,* pp. 153, 155, 156

*See *Materials to Prepare,* p. 77.

Classroom Routines

Quick Images: Tens and Ones Show Image J from *Quick Images 4: Tens and Ones* (T85). Follow the basic *Quick Images* activity. Students determine the total number of shaded squares and share their strategies. Record equations to represent the image, such as $80 + 7$. If no one mentions $100 - 13 = 87$, ask students how they could use subtraction to determine the number of shaded squares. Repeat for Images K and L.

Teaching Note

❶ Rulers For this unit, students need a ruler that is marked in inches on one side and centimeters on the other (or two different rulers, one marked in inches, one in centimeters). For Grade 2 students, a ruler marked only in whole inches and centimeters is easier to read and use while they are concentrating on what length is and what it means to measure length.

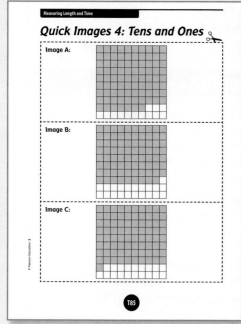

Measuring Length and Time

Quick Images 4: Tens and Ones ✂

Image A:

Image B:

Image C:

T85

▲ Transparencies, T85

ACTIVITY

① Inch-Bricks and Rulers

20 MIN PAIRS

Distribute rulers to each student.❶ Make sure that each student also has his or her Inch-brick measuring tool and a copy of *Student Activity Book* page 32.

In the story we read in the last session, the carpenter solved her problem by cutting a stick the length of the king's foot and using that as a measuring tool whenever she built something. In the story about the Land of Inch, the people used inch-bricks and created inch-brick measuring tools. Besides using the king's foot and inch-bricks, there are other things you can use to measure. What kinds of tools have you used to measure, and what kinds of things have you measured?

Elicit students' ideas about why they have used different measurement tools in different situations. Show students different tools (rulers, a tape measure, a yardstick) as they are mentioned.

Why did you use a tape measure, not a ruler, to measure your height?

This emphasizes that certain tools lend themselves to certain situations.

Students now work in pairs on *Student Activity Book* page 32, comparing their rulers to their inch-brick measuring tools.

ONGOING ASSESSMENT: Observing Students at Work

Students identify similarities and differences between a ruler and their inch-brick measuring tool.

- **Do students notice similarities between the tools?** That both tools are the same length? That both are numbered from 1 to 12? That the length of an inch-brick is the same as the distance between certain lines on a ruler?

- **Do students notice differences between the tools?** That the numbers appear at the end of the space instead of in the middle? Note that some of the differences that students identify might be nonmathematical, (e.g., color).

DIFFERENTIATION: Supporting the Range of Learners

Extension Students who easily find two similarities and two differences should be encouraged to identify more similarities.

Students learn to use different measuring tools in different situations.

DISCUSSION

2 Comparing Tools

15 MIN   CLASS

Math Focus Points for Discussion

◆ Becoming familiar with the terms *inches, feet,* and *yards* as standard units of measure

Ask students to discuss the similarities and differences they found between the ruler and the inch-brick measuring tool. The similarities students find are likely to be the significant features that are important to emphasize. In particular, have students notice which side of the ruler matches the length of an inch-brick.

When discussing the differences, ask students which differences matter when they measure something. For example, the color of the tool or the ruler does not matter. Students might mention that the flexibility of the inch-brick measuring tool can make a difference because it can be used like a measuring tape.

Name _____ Date _____

Measuring Length and Time

Rulers and Inch-Brick Measuring Tools ✎

Examine your ruler and your inch-brick measuring tool. Record your answers.

Name two things that are the same.

1. _____
   _____

2. _____
   _____

Name two things that are different.

1. _____
   _____

2. _____
   _____

32 Unit 9   Session 3.2

▲ Student Activity Book, p. 32 WRITING

Teaching Notes

② **Abbreviations for Units of Measure** As students discuss and record different units of measure throughout this Investigation, introduce the appropriate abbreviations (in., ft, yd, cm, m). You might write these on a chart that remains posted in the classroom throughout the rest of the unit. Encourage students to use these in their own recording; however, it is not expected that all second graders will use these fluently.

③ **Measuring Tools** Be careful not to confuse a yardstick (which is 1 yard long, equivalent to 3 feet or 36 inches) and a meter stick (which is 1 meter long, longer than 1 yard, approximately 39 inches).

Professional Development

④ **Teacher Note:** Benchmarks on the Body, p. 156
Teacher Note: Learning to Use a Ruler, p. 157

Name _____ Date _____
Measuring Length and Time

Body Benchmarks
Body benchmarks are parts of the body that you can sometimes use to measure objects if you do not have a ruler handy. Use body benchmarks to answer each question.

1. What on your body is about 1 inch long? _____

2. What on your body is about 6 inches long? _____

3. What on your body is about 12 inches (1 foot) long? _____

4. Use your body benchmark to measure your pencil.
   Estimated length: _____
   Use your ruler to measure your pencil.
   Measured length: _____

5. Use your body benchmark to measure the height of your chair.
   Estimated height: _____
   Use your ruler or a yardstick to measure the height of your chair.
   Measured height: _____

Sessions 3.2, 3.3   Unit 9 33

▲ **Student Activity Book, p. 33**

Point out to the students that on a 12-inch ruler, the unit that is numbered is called an inch and the unit that is the length of the ruler is called a foot.**②**

If your rulers have inches along one edge and centimeters along the other, or on reverse sides, call attention to both. Explain to students that they will be using both metric and U.S. standard measurements in this unit, but that first they will be measuring with inches and feet.

Distribute the yellow strips and blue strips that were used in Investigation 1 and ask students to use their rulers to measure the strips.

I'd like you to measure each of these strips and then record how long they are in inches on one side of the strip.

Ask a student to demonstrate how to use the ruler to show that the yellow strip is 3 inches long. Ask another student to demonstrate how to use the ruler to show that the blue strip is 6 inches long.

Hold up a yardstick and point out that this measuring tool is the length of another unit called a yard. Ask the class how many feet long they think a yard is. After hearing some ideas, have a student measure the yardstick with a ruler. Then ask the class how many inches long a yard is. Some students might figure it out by adding up 12 inches for each foot; some might choose to measure it. If students do not mention it, point out that 36 inches are labeled on the yardstick.**③**

MATH WORKSHOP

3 **Measuring**
25 MIN

Explain to the students that there are two workshop activities that they will continue in the next session.

3A **Body Benchmarks**
PAIRS

Students find their own personal "benchmark measurements" on their bodies.**④**

For Body Benchmarks, you'll be finding a part of your body that's about 1 inch long, a part that's about 6 inches long, and a part that's about 12 inches, or 1 foot, long. Sometimes, if we want to measure something and we don't have a ruler handy, we can use these body benchmarks instead.

Show an inch benchmark on your own body (e.g., perhaps a knuckle), and illustrate how you can measure an object using that benchmark. Then show your own benchmarks for 6 inches and 12 inches.

Point out the chart titled, "Body Benchmarks." Tell students they will record their body benchmarks on the chart and on *Student Activity Book* page 33. Then they will pick an object to measure with their body benchmark and record how long it is.

ONGOING ASSESSMENT: Observing Students at Work

Students find body benchmarks that measure about 1 inch, 6 inches, and 1 foot, and use these to measure objects.

- **Are students able to find parts of their bodies that correspond to 1 inch, to 6 inches, and to 12 inches?**

- **Once students have identified benchmarks, can they use their benchmarks to measure an object in feet and/or inches?**

- **When students measure the length of the object, do they write down the count and the unit (inches, feet)?**

Having students find benchmarks on their bodies helps them understand the units.

3B Measure and Compare

PAIRS

Students measure and compare the size of familiar objects in the classroom, recording their findings on *Student Activity Book* pages 34–35. Review the terms *length* and *width* with the students. ⑤

Professional Development

⑤ **Dialogue Box:** What's the Length and What's the Width?, p. 167

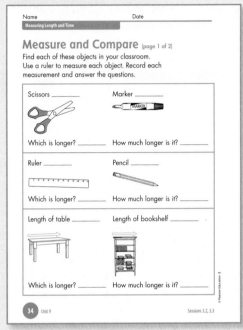

▲ Student Activity Book, p. 34

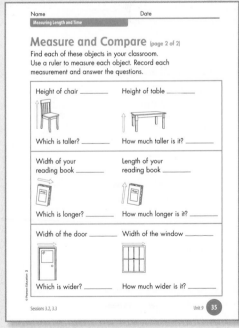

▲ Student Activity Book, p. 35

Teaching Note

⑥ Appropriate Estimation Students may find that they need to use fractional parts of an inch when they measure. However, knowing that an object is "about $3\frac{1}{2}$ inches" or "close to 4 inches" is an appropriate estimation for second graders.

Counting Money

How much money does each student have? How much more does each one need to make $1.00?

NOTE Students practice counting money and determining the difference between the amount they count and $1.00.
19, 21

1. Kira has _____
Kira needs _____ to make $1.00.

2. Jake has _____
Jake needs _____ to make $1.00.

3. Franco has _____
Franco needs _____ to make $1.00.

4. Sally has _____
Sally needs _____ to make $1.00.

36 Unit 9 · Session 3.2

▲ Student Activity Book, p. 36

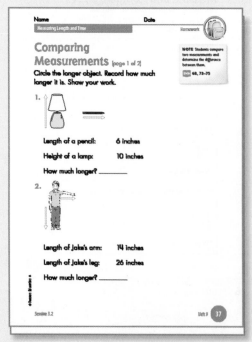

Comparing Measurements (page 1 of 2)

Circle the longer object. Record how much longer it is. Show your work.

NOTE Students compare two measurements and determine the difference between them.
68, 73–75

1. Length of a pencil: 6 inches
Height of a lamp: 10 inches
How much longer? _____

2. Length of Jake's arm: 14 inches
Length of Jake's leg: 26 inches
How much longer? _____

Session 3.2 · Unit 9 37

▲ Student Activity Book, pp. 37–38

For *Student Activity Book* pages 34–35, you will be measuring objects and then comparing their lengths. For each pair of objects you measure, you will say how much longer one object is than the other and show how you figured it out.

ONGOING ASSESSMENT: Observing Students at Work

Students use rulers to measure pairs of objects, and compare the two measurements.

- **Do they correctly align the end of the ruler with the end of the object?**

- **Do they start at zero?**

- **How do they measure objects longer than the length of the ruler?**

- **If your students are using rulers that have inches along one edge and centimeters along the other, or on reverse sides, do they mix up or combine the two units?**

DIFFERENTIATION: Supporting the Range of Learners

Intervention Some students may be able to determine the difference between lengths that involve fractional inches (e.g., the difference between a 12-inch ruler and a $7\frac{1}{2}$-inch pencil). If students have difficulty finding the difference when one or both lengths involve a partial inch, suggest that they round off to the nearest whole inch. ⑥

SESSION FOLLOW-UP

④ Daily Practice and Homework

Daily Practice: For ongoing review, have students complete *Student Activity Book* page 36.

Homework: For homework, students complete *Student Activity Book* pages 37–38. Students will compare two measurements and determine the difference between them.

Student Math Handbook: Students and families may use *Student Math Handbook* pages 153, 155, 156 for reference and review. See pages 172–178 in the back of this unit.

Measurement Strategies

Math Focus Points

◆ Using inches, feet, and yards to describe lengths

◆ Measuring lengths that are longer than 12 inches

Today's Plan		Materials
① DISCUSSION **Measurement Strategies**	🕐 10 MIN 👥 CLASS	
② MATH WORKSHOP **More Measuring** **2A** Body Benchmarks **2B** Measure and Compare **2C** Measuring Our Classroom	🕐 40 MIN	**2A** • *Student Activity Book,* p. 33 (from Session 3.2) • Chart: "Body Benchmarks" (from Session 3.2); rulers **2B** • *Student Activity Book,* pp. 34–35 (from Session 3.2) • Rulers **2C** • *Student Activity Book,* p. 39 • Rulers or yardsticks
③ DISCUSSION **Measuring Our Classroom**	🕐 10 MIN 👥 CLASS	
④ SESSION FOLLOW-UP **Daily Practice and Homework**		• *Student Activity Book,* pp. 40–42 • *Student Math Handbook,* pp. 153, 156, 157

Classroom Routines

Today's Number: 32 Using Subtraction Individually students generate expressions
for 32 using subtraction and several numbers (e.g., 50 − 10 − 8, or 62 − 20 − 10).
For each expression they write a corresponding expression using only two numbers
(e.g., 50 − 10 − 8 = 50 − 18 or 62 − 20 − 10 = 62 − 30).

Professional Development

❶ **Dialogue Box:** Measuring Lengths Longer than 24 Inches, p. 169

DISCUSSION

❶ Measurement Strategies

10 MIN CLASS

Math Focus Points for Discussion

◆ Measuring lengths that are longer than 12 inches

Based on your observations in Session 3.2, ask several students how they would measure their desktop or the tabletop.❶ Choose students whom you observed using different strategies and approaches. As students demonstrate their measuring techniques, you can highlight important strategies by commenting and questioning as they demonstrate. For example:

I noticed that [Jacy] made sure to line up the beginning of the ruler with the very edge of the desk.

[Chen] used his finger to mark the end of the ruler, and then he moved the beginning of the ruler to that point so he could continue measuring.

Encourage students to try different ways to measure large objects.

I see that [Katrina] is being careful not to leave any space between where one ruler ends and where the next one begins.

Can you explain how you figured that your desk was 21 inches long if you measured that it was 1 foot plus 9 inches?

If your students do not mention the yardstick as a tool that is good for measuring things longer than a foot, you should suggest it as another measuring tool. If you did not discuss the yardstick in the previous session, have students measure the length of the yardstick to see that it is 3 feet or 36 inches.

MATH WORKSHOP

② More Measuring

40 MIN

In addition to the two workshop activities from Session 3.2, students will work on a third, Measuring Our Classroom.

2A Body Benchmarks

PAIRS

For complete details about this activity, see Session 3.2, page 88.

2B Measure and Compare

PAIRS

For complete details about this activity, see Session 3.2, page 89.

2C Measuring Our Classroom

PAIRS

Students measure the length or width of the classroom and record their findings on *Student Activity Book* page 39. Choose one dimension of your classroom (length or width) for students to measure. Review the terms *how wide* or *width* with students, and point out the length and width of the classroom as you introduce this activity.

✓ ONGOING ASSESSMENT: Observing Students at Work

Students use measurement tools to measure the length or width of the classroom.

- **Do students use rulers, or do they choose to use a yardstick for this activity?**

- **How do they iterate the tool they are using?** Do they flip the unit end over end? Do they place a finger or marker at the end of the unit, then pick it up and place it so that the starting end of the unit is at that point?

- **Do students count inches, feet, or yards?**

- **How do students keep track of how many units they have measured?**

Name _____ Date _____

Measuring Length and Time

Measuring Our Classroom ✏

Choose a unit to measure the length or width of your classroom.

1. Did you measure the length or width of the classroom? _____

2. What unit did you use to measure the classroom? _____

3. What was the measurement? _____

4. Describe how you measured the classroom.

_____
_____
_____
_____
_____
_____
_____
_____

Session 3.3   Unit 9   **39**

▲ **Student Activity Book, p. 39**

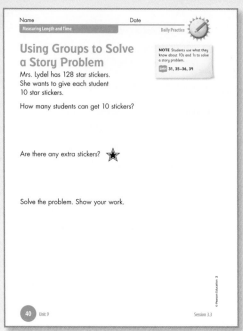

▲ Student Activity Book, p. 40

DIFFERENTIATION: Supporting the Range of Learners

Intervention This may be too large a measuring task for some students. Consider pairing students or assigning a smaller aspect of the classroom to measure. The length/width of an area rug, the length of the chalk or bulletin board, or the width of a doorway may be more manageable tasks that will give students direct experiences with measuring larger objects. Additionally, you can offer students multiple *units* or multiple rulers/yardsticks that they can lay end-to-end to measure large spaces.

Extension For those students needing more of a challenge, suggest that they compare the size of different classrooms to determine which space they think is bigger. Have them write an explanation to support their findings.

ELL In this discussion, students need to understand words such as *beginning, end, edge, mark, space,* and *next.* You can demonstrate this vocabulary during Math Workshop by thinking aloud with English Language Learners as you help them measure an object or two. Let's see how long this table is. We need to put the *beginning* of the ruler at the very *edge* of the desk. Can you *mark* the *end* of the ruler with your finger? I'll move the ruler so we can keep measuring. Let's be careful not to leave any *spaces.* Okay, let's measure this *next* part together.

Using a yardstick makes it easier to measure large areas.

DISCUSSION

③ Measuring Our Classroom

10 MIN   CLASS

Math Focus Points for Discussion

◆ Measuring lengths that are longer than 12 inches

Spend the last 10 minutes of the session discussing issues that arose as students measured the length or width of the classroom. If students got different results, have them describe their measurement strategies to find where the discrepancy arose. If some students measured in inches and others in feet or yards (e.g., 360 inches, 30 feet, 10 yards), discuss whether their measurements are equivalent.

SESSION FOLLOW-UP

④ Daily Practice and Homework

Daily Practice: For ongoing review, have students complete *Student Activity Book* page 40.

Homework: For homework, students complete *Student Activity Book* pages 41–42. They will use body benchmarks to estimate and then a ruler to measure the length and width of any three rectangular objects at home.

Student Math Handbook: Students and families may use *Student Math Handbook* pages 153, 156, 157 for reference and review. See pages 172–178 in the back of this unit.

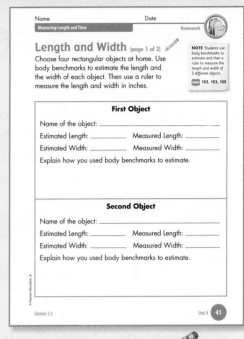

▲ Student Activity Book, p. 41

▲ Student Activity Book, p. 42

Moving to Metric

Math Focus Points

◆ Becoming familiar with the terms *centimeters* and *meters* as standard units of measure

◆ Comparing centimeters and inches

◆ Using centimeters and meters to describe length

Vocabulary

metric system
centimeter
meter

Today's Plan		Materials
① DISCUSSION **Meters and Centimeters** 🕐 10 MIN 👪 CLASS		• M16* • World map or globe (optional); centimeter cubes (as needed); rulers
② ACTIVITY **Creating Metric Tools** 🕐 10 MIN 👤 INDIVIDUALS		• M16 • Meter strip*; scissors; tape

③ MATH WORKSHOP
Metric Measures   🕐 40 MIN
   3A Metric Scavenger Hunt
   3B Comparing Tools
		3A • *Student Activity Book*, p. 43
		  • Charts: "Things About 1 Centimeter Long in School" and "Things About 1 Meter Long in School"*; meter strips (from Activity 2); metersticks
		3B • *Student Activity Book*, p. 44
		  • Rulers

④ SESSION FOLLOW-UP **Daily Practice and Homework**		• *Student Activity Book*, pp. 45–46 • *Student Math Handbook*, p. 154 • Meter strips (from Activity 2)

*See *Materials to Prepare*, p. 77.

Classroom Routines

What Time Is It?: What Time Will It Be? Write 8:15 on the board. Ask students to set their clocks to that time. Then ask,

What time will it be in one and a half hours?

Ask students to set the new time on their clocks and discuss with their partner how they determined the time and how the hands moved on the clock. Record the new time (9:45) on the board. Repeat for times beginning at 10:15 and 2:15.

DISCUSSION

① Meters and Centimeters

10 MIN   CLASS

Math Focus Points for Discussion

◆ Becoming familiar with the terms *centimeters* and *meters* as standard units of measure

If you have students from other countries, they might be familiar with the metric system and could take a leadership role in this discussion.

Remember that in the story, "The King's Foot," the king and the carpenter had different ideas of how large the horse stall should be. What was the problem?

Students might say:

"Their feet were different sizes. They could not agree whose foot to use to measure."

Review the story briefly and encourage students to explain what happens when people do not agree on a standard unit of measure.

People in the United States have agreed to use inches and feet and yards to measure. But other people all around the world have a different system for measuring. It's called the metric system, and it uses units like centimeters and meters. Only a few other countries besides the United States in the whole world use inches, feet, and yards instead of centimeters and meters.

If students are curious about why there are only a few countries that use the nonmetric (U.S. standard) system, you may want to give them some background on this.❶

Ask students whether they know how long a centimeter is. Ask students who know to show the class. If no one knows, show them centimeter cubes or point to the squares on centimeter grid paper. Point out that one centimeter is the length of the edge of a cube or the length of the side of a square on the grid paper. Explain that this is the metric unit that we use when we are measuring something small.

Give each student a sheet of Centimeter Grid Paper (M16) and a ruler that has one side marked in inches and one side marked in centimeters. Point out that until now, they have been using the side of the ruler marked in inches. Have students now use the centimeter side of the ruler

Professional Development

❶ **Teacher Note:** Background on the Metric System, p. 158

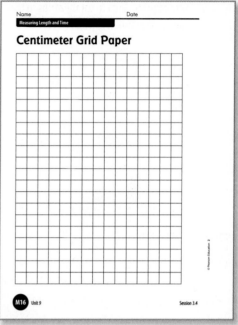

▲ Resource Masters, M16

to measure the squares on the grid paper. Explain that when measuring larger things, like rooms, we use meters. Show the meterstick.

A meter is a little longer than a yard, and it is made up of 100 centimeters.

Students learn that most of the world uses metric measurements.

ACTIVITY

❷ Creating Metric Tools

10 MIN   INDIVIDUALS

Today you're going to have two scavenger hunts—one at school and one at home. You'll search for things that are about 1 meter long and about 1 centimeter long. In case you don't have the tools you'll need at home, we're going to make a paper *meter strip* for you to use.

Show students the meter strip you prepared. Do not tell them how you cut the grid paper to make your strip. Ask them how they could use grid paper to make a similar strip 1 meter long. Encourage them to use their knowledge of how long and wide the grid is—20 centimeter blocks by 15 centimeter blocks—to figure out how to construct a 100-centimeter strip.❷ This is a good opportunity to review how the number 100 is composed of groups of 20.

ONGOING ASSESSMENT: Observing Students at Work

Students create meter strips using centimeter grid paper.

- **Do students use what they know about 100 to create a strip 100 centimeters long?**

MATH WORKSHOP
③ Metric Measures

40 MIN

Students develop their awareness of metric measures through the two workshop activities. They will continue the Metric Scavenger Hunt for homework. In the next session, they will discuss what they found comparing the inch- and centimeter-sides of their rulers.

3A Metric Scavenger Hunt

INDIVIDUALS

Post the prepared charts with the headings, "Things About 1 Centimeter Long in School" and "Things About 1 Meter Long in School" where students can write on them.

Students work individually to look for things in the classroom that are about 1 meter long and 1 centimeter long, recording their findings on *Student Activity Book* page 43. The objects do not have to be *exactly* these sizes—encourage students to find things that are *approximately* the right size. Have students each write one result of their hunt on the appropriate chart.

Before students start to use their meter strips, have them compare their strips to the meterstick to check for accuracy. If you have enough metersticks in the classroom, have students save their paper meter strips to use for homework because the paper strips are not very sturdy.

Students look for and measure objects that are 1 centimeter long and 1 meter long.

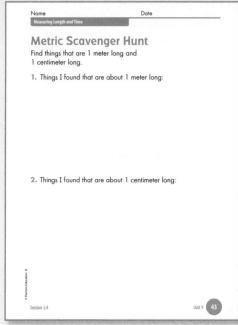

▲ **Student Activity Book, p. 43**

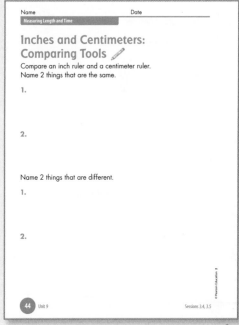

▲ **Student Activity Book, p. 44**

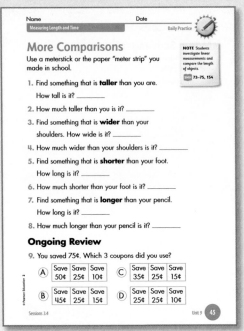

▲ Student Activity Book, p. 45

▲ Student Activity Book, p. 46

ONGOING ASSESSMENT: Observing Students at Work

Students identify objects that are about 1 centimeter in length and about 1 meter in length.

- **Are students able to estimate lengths that are approximately 1 centimeter and 1 meter?**

3B Comparing Tools

PAIRS

Working in pairs, students place their rulers next to each other, one ruler with inches showing, the other with centimeters showing. Students record on *Student Activity Book* page 44 the similarities and differences they notice.

ONGOING ASSESSMENT: Observing Students at Work

Students compare centimeters and inches.

- **What similarities do students notice between the two sides of the second-grade ruler?** Do they notice that both mark off units of equal length? Do they notice that the units are numbered, starting at 1?

- **What differences do students notice between the two sides of the second-grade ruler?** Do they notice that centimeters are smaller than inches? Do they notice that more centimeters than inches fit on a ruler (e.g., the count of the centimeters is higher)?

SESSION FOLLOW-UP
4 Daily Practice and Homework

Daily Practice: For reinforcement of this unit's content, have students complete *Student Activity Book* page 45.

Homework: For homework, students will conduct a Metric Scavenger Hunt at home and record their findings on *Student Activity Book* page 46. They will need to take home their paper meter strips.

Student Math Handbook: Students and families may use *Student Math Handbook* page 154 for reference and review. See pages 172–178 in the back of this unit.

Metric Measurement

Math Focus Points

- ◆ Comparing a variety of measuring tools
- ◆ Using inches and centimeters to describe length
- ◆ Comparing centimeters and inches
- ◆ Understanding that different-sized units yield different counts (the smaller the unit, the higher the count)

Today's Plan		Materials
DISCUSSION **① Comparing Tools**	15 MIN CLASS	• *Student Activity Book,* pp. 44 and 46 (from Session 3.4) • Charts: "Things About 1 Centimeter Long at Home," and "Things About 1 Meter Long at Home"*
ACTIVITY **② Measuring with Inches and Centimeters**	25 MIN PAIRS	• *Student Activity Book,* p. 47 • Rulers; pencil; book; scissors
DISCUSSION **③ Inches and Centimeters**	20 MIN CLASS	• *Student Activity Book,* p. 47 (from Activity 2) • Chart paper*
SESSION FOLLOW-UP **④ Daily Practice**		• *Student Activity Book,* p. 48 • *Student Math Handbook,* pp. 150–151, 153, 154, 155

*See *Materials to Prepare,* p. 77.

Classroom Routines

Quick Images: Tens and Ones Show Image M from *Quick Images 5: Tens and Ones* (T86). Follow the basic *Quick Images* activity. Students determine the total number of shaded squares and share their strategies. Record equations to represent the image, such as $60 + 5 = 65$. If no one mentions $100 - 35 = 65$, ask students how they could use subtraction to determine the number of shaded squares. Repeat for Images N and O.

Student Activity Book Worksheet

Name _____ **Date** _____

Measuring Length and Time

Inches and Centimeters: Measuring ✏️

Measure each object. Record your measurements.

1. Your pencil is _____ inches long.

   Your pencil is _____ centimeters long.
   Circle the unit that gives you the larger number.

   inches   centimeters

2. Your book is _____ inches long.

   Your book is _____ centimeters long.
   Circle the unit that gives you the larger number.

   inches   centimeters

3. Your scissors are _____ inches long.

   Your scissors are _____ centimeters long.
   Circle the unit that gives you the larger number.

   inches   centimeters

4. Which unit always gives you the larger number?

   inches   centimeters

5. Why do you think this happens?

   _____
   _____
   _____

Session 3.5   Unit 9   47

▲ **Student Activity Book, p. 47** WRITING

---

1 Comparing Tools

Math Focus Points for Discussion

◆ Comparing a variety of measuring tools

At the beginning of the day, post the prepared charts with the headings, "Things About 1 Centimeter Long at Home" and "Things About 1 Meter Long at Home" where students can write on them. As students arrive in class, have them write the results of their home scavenger hunt on these charts.

Was it hard or easy to find things that were about one centimeter long? About one meter long? What are the differences between the things you found at home and at school?

Now have students turn to their completed work from the previous session on *Student Activity Book* page 44.

Focus on the similarities and then the differences that students found between the two sides of the ruler. Students are likely to bring up some non-mathematical differences, such as the color, design, etc. Although these are definitely differences, they are not features that need attention while measuring. Help students distinguish between those differences that are irrelevant to measuring and those that are important to measuring. For example, both sides of the ruler repeatedly mark off units and those units are numbered starting at 1. They also may notice that centimeters are smaller than inches and that the centimeter side has higher numbers than the inch side. Some students may observe that this means there are more centimeters than inches on the ruler.

2 Measuring with Inches and Centimeters

For the remainder of the session, students work on *Student Activity Book* page 47. Students measure their pencil, a book, and scissors in both inches and centimeters. They identify which measurement has the larger number and explain why. Make sure that any pair of students measures the *same* items in both inches and centimeters. Different pairs might measure pencils, books, or scissors of different lengths.

ONGOING ASSESSMENT: Observing Students at Work

Students measure objects with both inches and centimeters.

- **Do students use the ruler appropriately?**

- **Do they measure accurately with both inches and centimeters?**

- **Do they recognize that, when an object is measured, there are more centimeters than inches because a centimeter is a smaller unit of measure than an inch?**

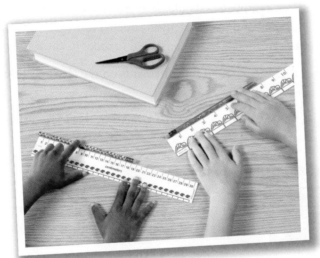

When students use different units (inch or centimeter ruler) to measure the same object, they learn to expect different counts.

DISCUSSION

Inches and Centimeters

20 MIN   CLASS

Math Focus Points for Discussion

◆ Comparing centimeters and inches

◆ Understanding that different-sized units yield different counts (the smaller the unit, the higher the count)

Ask several students to share the measurements they got—in inches and in centimeters—for their pencils, books, and scissors and record them on the 6-column chart. Have a few students demonstrate how they measured their pencils, books, or scissors.

▲ **Student Activity Book, p. 48**

Pencil		Book		Scissors	
Inches	Centimeters	Inches	Centimeters	Inches	Centimeters

Since pairs of students may have measured objects of different lengths, their measurements may be different. However, since they were to measure the same object in inches and in centimeters, for any given object, the number of centimeters should be approximately 2.5 times the number of inches. If any of the measurements offered seem very far off, include them as measurements to be demonstrated in order to correct them.

Once there are enough measurements on the chart, ask the students what they notice.

Which measurements give the larger number? Does that always happen? Why do you think it works that way?

Students might say:

"Centimeters give the larger number because centimeters are smaller than inches."

Point out to students that in the last few weeks, they have done a lot of work figuring out how to measure length. Ask them to identify some of the things they have learned. They might say that they learned:

- How to use a ruler
- How to measure accurately
- About inches, feet, yards, centimeters, and meters
- That the smaller unit yields the larger count.

SESSION FOLLOW-UP

 4 Daily Practice

 Daily Practice: For reinforcement of this unit's content, have students complete *Student Activity Book* page 48.

Student Math Handbook: Students and families may use *Student Math Handbook* pages 150–151, 153, 154, 155 for reference and review. See pages 172–178 in the back of this unit.

Mathematical Emphasis

Time Representing time and calculating duration

Math Focus Points

◆ Representing time as a horizontal sequence

◆ Connecting a time, its digital notation, and its representation on an analog clock to a timeline

◆ Using a timeline to determine duration

◆ Associating times with daily events

◆ Moving forward and backward along a timeline in multiples of hours, half hours, and quarter hours

◆ Using a timeline to show a 24-hour period

◆ Recording events on a timeline

◆ Naming and using notation for times that are 30 and 15 minutes before or after the hour

Representing Time

	Student Activity Book	Student Math Handbook	Professional Development: Read Ahead of Time	
SESSION 4.1 p. 110				
A Timeline Tells a Story Students listen to a story as an introduction to timelines and representing time as a horizontal sequence. They represent the schedule of their school day on a timeline, focusing on intervals of 1 hour.	49–50	143, 144, 145	• **Teacher Note:** Working with Timelines, p. 159	
SESSION 4.2 p. 116				
Hours of the Day and Night Students extend their school day timelines to include hours before and after school. They work with hour and half-hour intervals as they discuss the time and duration of daily events.	50–52	142, 143, 144, 145		
SESSION 4.3 p. 121				
Fred & Winnipeg Timelines The class is introduced to Fred and Winnipeg stories about the daily activities of two cats. Students work on timeline problems using the stories.	53–61	142, 143, 144, 145	• **Dialogue Box:** Not Even a Second Has Gone By: Calculating Duration, p. 170	
SESSION 4.4 p. 126				
Solving Timeline Problems Students are introduced to quarter hours on the timeline. They extend the Full Day Timeline in both directions to complete a day from midnight to midnight. Students work on problems involving a 24-hour timeline for Fred and Winnipeg.	62–65	136, 137–138, 139, 140, 142, 143, 144, 145		

Classroom Routines See page 16 for an overview.

Today's Number
- M18, *Today's Number: 72* Make copies. (1 per student)

What Time Is It?
- **Student Clocks** (1 per pair)
- **Demonstration Clock**
- **School Day Timelines (from Session 4.1)**

Materials to Gather	Materials to Prepare
• **Demonstration clock** • **Scissors** (1 per student) • **Glue or tape** (1 per student) • **Chart paper** (optional)	• **M17, School Day Timeline** Make copies. (1 per student) You may want to assemble timelines for students who will have difficulty cutting and pasting their own together. Use copies to enlarge the timeline for students who need more room to write. • **Children's book** Select a book or prepare a story to read to the class that depicts a character's actions over a day. Possible books include *Telling Time with Big Mama Cat* by Dan Harper or *Alexander and the Terrible, Horrible, No-Good, Very Bad Day* by Judith Viorst. • **Chart paper** Title the chart "School Day Schedule." Create a school day schedule that includes times that fall on the hour, with a limited number of times that fall on the half hour. List each event on a proportional piece of cardstock or sketch them on the board or chart paper. The size of the largest piece should be for the subject that lasts the longest, with other pieces proportional. See page 112. • **Chart paper** Create a large School Day Timeline to post in the classroom with tick marks on the hour and half hour. Make one hour the same length as your cardstock label for a one-hour event. Include digital notation for each hour, from 8:00 A.M. to 3:00 P.M. Under 12:00 P.M., write "Noon." Leave room to extend this timeline later (from midnight to midnight). See page 113.
• **Demonstration clock** • **Scissors** (1 per student) • **Glue or tape** (1 per student)	• **Full Day Timeline** Extend the School Day Timeline from 5:00 A.M. on the left to 9:00 P.M. on the right. Include tick marks every half hour. If there are space constraints, you can continue the timeline on a second line. Leave room to extend further in both directions. See page 117. • **M19, Timeline for Morning and Evening Activities** Makes copies. (1 per student)
• **T87, Fred & Winnipeg: Chapter 1** • **T88, Fred & Winnipeg: Chapter 1 Timeline** • **Student Clocks** (as needed) • **Demonstration Clock**	• **M22, Fred & Winnipeg: Chapter 2** Make copies. (1 per student; optional) • **M23, Fred & Winnipeg: Chapter 2, List of Events** Make copies. (as needed) • **M24, Fred & Winnipeg: Chapter 3** Make copies. (1 per student; optional) • **M25, Fred & Winnipeg: Chapter 3, List of Events** Make copies. (1 per student; optional)
• **T89, How Long Is It? Quarter Hours** • **Student Clocks** (as needed) • **Full Day Timeline** (from Session 4.2) • **Chart paper**	• **M27–M28, A Fred & Winnipeg Timeline** Make copies. (1 per student)

 Overhead Transparency

Representing Time, *continued*

SESSION 4.5 p. 134	Student Activity Book	Student Math Handbook	Professional Development: Read Ahead of Time	
Special Day Timelines Students work on problems involving duration and timelines over a 24-hour period. They create timelines with events from their own special day.	65, 67	136, 137–138, 139, 140, 142, 143, 144, 145		
SESSION 4.6 p. 139				
Comparing Special Day Timelines Students finish their Special Day Timelines and compare the timelines of classmates by answering questions about durations.	65, 68–69	143, 144, 145		
SESSION 4.7 p. 143				
End-of-Unit Assessment Students work on two problems as an End-of-Unit Assessment. The first involves measuring a line, using both inches and centimeters. The second focuses on timelines. Students answer questions about someone's day and then fill in the events on the timeline.	70	144, 145, 155, 156	• **Teacher Note:** End-of-Unit Assessment, p. 160	

Materials to Gather	Materials to Prepare
• **T89, How Long Is It? Quarter Hours** 🖨 • **24-Hour Timeline** (from Session 4.3) • **Student Clocks** (1 per student) • **Scissors** (1 per student) • **Glue or tape** (1 per student)	• **M29–M30, Special Day Timelines** Make copies. (1 per student). You may want to assemble timelines for students who will have difficulty cutting and pasting their own together. Use copies to enlarge the timeline for students who need more room to write.
• **T90, Maria's Timeline** 🖨 • **Demonstration Clock** • **Special Day Timelines** (1 per student; from Session 4.5)	• **Display Space** Plan a space to display Special Day Timelines.
• **Rulers** (1 per student)	• **M32–M35, End-of-Unit Assessment** Make copies. (1 per student) • **Strips of adding machine tape** Cut into 17-inch lengths. (1 per student)

🖨 Overhead Transparency

A Timeline Tells a Story

Math Focus Points

- Representing time as a horizontal sequence
- Connecting a time, its digital notation, and its representation on an analog clock to a timeline

Today's Plan		Materials
ACTIVITY ❶ **Introducing Timelines** 20 MIN CLASS		• Demonstration clock; chart paper (optional); children's book* (optional)
ACTIVITY ❷ **A Timeline for the School Day** 40 MIN CLASS INDIVIDUALS		• M17* • Charts: "School Day Schedule"* and School Day Timeline*; demonstration clock; scissors; glue or tape
SESSION FOLLOW-UP ❸ **Daily Practice and Homework**		• *Student Activity Book*, pp. 49–50 • *Student Math Handbook*, pp. 143, 144, 145

*See *Materials to Prepare*, p. 107.

Classroom Routines

Today's Number: 72 Students individually complete *Today's Number: 72* (M18), which reflects much of their work with *Today's Number* over the course of this year. This is the ninth in a series of work samples for *Today's Number* that has been collected throughout the year.

ACTIVITY

1 Introducing Timelines

20 MIN   CLASS

As an introduction to this Investigation, tell a story about the events in the day of someone's life. You could tell a story about a day in your life, maybe a day from a past weekend, read a children's book that depicts someone's day, or create a story based on a favorite character of your students. The story should mention specific times that some events occurred.

Here is an example of a possible story.

I'm going to tell you what I did on Saturday. I woke up at 9:00 A.M. and I took my shower and ate breakfast. Then at 10:00 A.M., I did my laundry and got ready to go out. An hour later, at 11:00 A.M., I got on a bus to go downtown to the parade.

I got downtown at noon and met a friend there. We watched the parade together from noon to 1:00 P.M. It was so crowded! At 1:00 P.M., we decided to go for a walk and find something to eat. We were walking for an entire hour before we found a restaurant we both wanted to go to! What time were we walking until? 2:00 P.M.!

I was so hungry. We sat in the restaurant for two hours until 4:00 P.M. Then I took a bus back home, and I got home at 5:00 P.M. I watched TV for half an hour until 5:30 P.M.

After telling the story or reading the book, ask students to repeat some of the events. Begin a list as students recall the various events of the story.

Let's put these events in order across the board. I'll put the first event on the left and the last event on the right.

List the events horizontally in order of their occurrence on the board [or chart paper] from left to right in a long row. If any times are mentioned in the story, ask students if they can recall the times, and note the times under the corresponding events.

What time do you think I was showering and eating breakfast?

Woke Up	Shower and Breakfast	Laundry and Get Ready to Go Out	On Bus	At Parade	Walking	Restaurant	On Bus	TV
9:00 A.M.	9:00–10:00	10:00–11:00	11:00–12:00	12:00–1:00	1:00–2:00	2:00–4:00	4:00–5:00	5:00–5:30

As students recall the times of the events, ask a student to use the demonstration clock to show the time at the beginning of the event

---

Today's Number: 72

Write 3 expressions in each box for the number 72.

Write 3 ways to make 72.	Use pennies, nickels, dimes, or quarters to make 72¢.
Use only subtraction to make 72.	Use only addition with at least 3 numbers to make 72.
Fill in the missing number. 100 − _____ = 72 40 + _____ = 72 59 + _____ = 72	Use only dimes and pennies to make 72¢.

M18   Unit 9   Session 4.1

▲ **Resource Masters, M18** PORTFOLIO

Professional Development

❶ **Teacher Note:** Working with Timelines, p. 159

and the time at the end of the event. If you are using a story in which the time for an event is not mentioned, ask students to guess what time the event may have occurred.

In my story, I began to do laundry at ten o'clock. Who can show me ten o'clock on the analog clock?

We have just made a timeline of the story. One way people have of showing time is to show events in order from left to right. We're going to be working on timelines in our next few math classes.

ACTIVITY

❷ A Timeline for the School Day

In this activity, students develop a timeline of the school day. In Sessions 4.2, 4.4, and 4.5, students extend this timeline to include events in their lives before and after school.❶

Draw students' attention to the "School Day Schedule" you have posted.

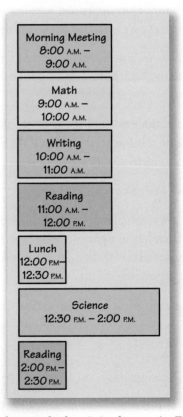

This isn't our schedule exactly, but it is close to it. For this activity, we're going to pretend that this is our school day schedule.

Next draw students' attention to the large School Day Timeline you prepared, and ask them about the units that they see on the timeline.

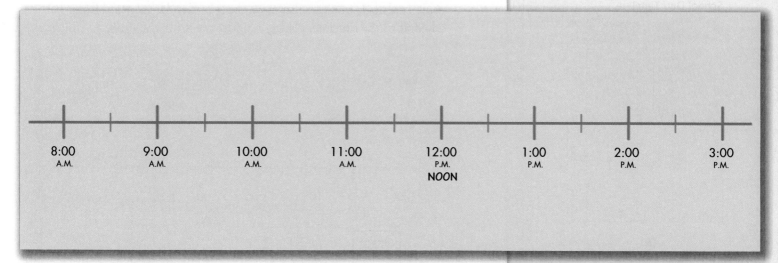

| 8:00 A.M. | 9:00 A.M. | 10:00 A.M. | 11:00 A.M. | 12:00 P.M. NOON | 1:00 P.M. | 2:00 P.M. | 3:00 P.M. |

This is a timeline. A timeline is a way to show different events and the time of day that they happened. What do you notice about this timeline? What do you notice about the times that appear on all of the longer slash lines? What times are represented by the smaller slashes in between?

Students might say:

"I see hours on the timeline."

How many minutes are in 1 hour?

Use the demonstration clock to count 60 minutes in an hour using 5-minute intervals. Count each number on the clock as 5 minutes to count up to 60 minutes.

The school day begins at 8:00 A.M. Where is 8:00 A.M. on the timeline?

Write "*School Begins*" at 8:00 A.M. on the timeline.❷

Look at our schedule. What time does *Morning Meeting* begin? What time does it end?

Ask one student to show the times using the demonstration clock. Ask another student to show these times on the timeline.

Teaching Note

❷ **Marking Times** To mark an event that occurs in one moment, such as when school begins, use a tick mark or an arrow with a clear label. For events of duration, such as *Morning Meeting*, use a bracket or curve to connect the two times.

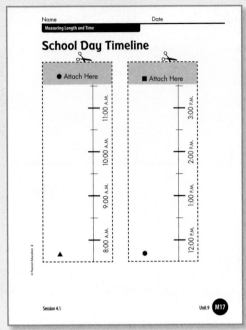

▲ Resource Masters, M17

Teaching Notes

❸ **Preparation Assistance** Some students may have difficulty cutting and preparing their own School Day Timeline. If this is the case prepare their timelines ahead of time using School Day Timeline (M17). In addition, you may want to prepare other timelines used in this Investigation using Timeline for Morning and Evening Activities (M19) and Special Day Timeline (M29–M30). For students requiring more room on their timelines to write events, make enlarged copies of the timeline. Enlarge the timeline to 30% and print on $8\frac{1}{2}$" x 14" paper.

❹ **Extending the Timeline** Students will add on to this School Day Timeline in the next session for the hours before and after the school day, using the square and triangle icons.

Mark the first event on the timeline by using a bracket or curve to connect 8:00 A.M. and 9:00 A.M. If you have prepared the Daily Schedule using cardstock, you can also move the *Morning Meeting* card from the schedule to the timeline, placing it under the 8:00 A.M.–9:00 A.M. interval.

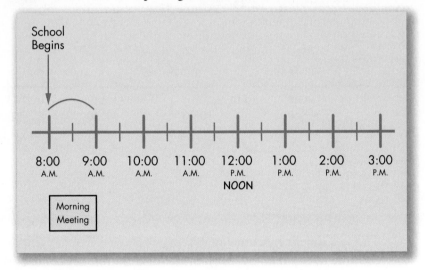

According to our schedule, what happens next after *Morning Meeting?* What time does math begin? What time does it end? How can I write this on the timeline?

Again, ask one student to show these times on the analog clock and another to show it on the timeline. Bracket the 9:00 A.M.–10:00 A.M. time on the timeline and label it "Math."

Mark at least one more example on the timeline before students work individually. Move the appropriate cardstock label or write in the event above the timeline.

Explain to students that for the remainder of the session they will make their own timelines for the school day, using School Day Timeline (M17).

Students need to cut the timeline pieces, and then glue or tape them together. Demonstrate how to glue or tape the beginning of the second piece that starts with "12:00 P.M." to the grey portion of the first piece, lining up the circle icons so that the times move forward chronologically. ❸ ❹

Students write half hours in digital notation and then add the rest of the events from the "School Day Schedule" to their timeline.

ONGOING ASSESSMENT: Observing Students at Work

Students use their timelines to show the events of the school day.

- **Do students glue/tape the timeline so that the times are chronological?**

- **Are students able to mark events on the timeline for appropriate durations?**

- **Can students read information on the timeline about the Daily Schedule?**

As you observe students, ask them questions about when events begin or end and the duration of an event.

How many hours did math last? How many minutes is that?

SESSION FOLLOW-UP
3 Daily Practice and Homework

 Daily Practice: For reinforcement of this unit's content, have students complete *Student Activity Book* page 49.

 Homework: Students will use *Student Activity Book* page 50 to write the beginning and ending times for common events in their day that occur in the morning and evening. The homework has spaces for events that are likely to take place in all households. There are additional spaces for students to write activities that they choose. Students may need to check with parents about the times certain events occur. They will use this homework in Session 4.2 to add information to the timeline that they began today.❹

 Student Math Handbook: Students and families may use *Student Math Handbook* pages 143, 144, 145 for reference and review. See pages 172–178 in the back of this unit.

Teaching Note

❹ **Terminology** Explain to the class that "Getting Ready for School" includes such things as brushing your teeth, getting dressed, and eating breakfast, which are typically done within a concentrated span of time.

Name _____ Date _____
Measuring Length and Time   Daily Practice

Whose Foot Is It?

NOTE Students compare and describe measurements numerically, and find the shortest and longest.

1. Read the following clues.
   - Pepe's foot is 2 centimeters shorter than Amy's foot.
   - Rick's foot is the same length as Amy's foot.
   - TJ's foot is 1 centimeter longer than Pepe's foot.
   - Rosario's foot is longer than Amy's foot, but shorter than Ben's foot.
   - Max's foot is the smallest of all!

2. Now write the person's name by the measurement that shows how long their foot is.

   17 centimeters _____

   18 centimeters _____

   19 centimeters _____

   20 centimeters _____

   20 centimeters _____

   21 centimeters _____

   22 centimeters _____

Ongoing Review

3. What time is 3 hours after 9:00 A.M.?

   Ⓐ 1:30 P.M.   Ⓒ 11:00 A.M.

   Ⓑ 12:00 P.M.   Ⓓ 10:30 A.M.

Session 4.1   Unit 9   49

▲ **Student Activity Book, p. 49**

Name _____ Date _____
Measuring Length and Time   Homework

Times for Morning and Evening Activities

For each activity, write the time it begins and ends.

NOTE Students write times for events that occur in their lives before and after school. Students will use this information in our next math class.

SMH 144

Before School

1. Wake up: Time: _____

2. Get ready for school: Begin: _____ End: _____
   (including brushing your
   teeth, getting dressed,
   and eating breakfast)

3. Ride or walk to school: Begin: _____ End: _____

After School

4. Ride or walk home: Begin: _____ End: _____

5. Eat dinner: Begin: _____ End: _____

Write in any other activities you did.

6. Activity: _____   Begin: _____ End: _____

7. Activity: _____   Begin: _____ End: _____

50   Unit 9   Sessions 4.1, 4.2

▲ **Student Activity Book, p. 50**

Hours of the Day and Night

Math Focus Points

◆ Connecting a time, its digital notation, and its representation on an analog clock to a timeline

◆ Using a timeline to determine duration

◆ Associating times with daily events

Vocabulary

half hour

A.M.

P.M.

Today's Plan			Materials
ACTIVITY **① Hours of the Day and Night**	🕐 20 MIN	👥 CLASS	• *Student Activity Book*, p. 50 (from Session 4.1) • Full Day Timeline*; demonstration clock
ACTIVITY **② A Timeline for Our Day**	🕐 40 MIN	🧍 INDIVIDUALS	• *Student Activity Book*, p. 50 (from Session 4.1) • M19* • Students' School Day Timelines (from Session 4.1); scissors; glue or tape
SESSION FOLLOW-UP **③ Daily Practice and Homework**			• *Student Activity Book*, pp. 51–52 • *Student Math Handbook*, pp. 142–145

*See *Materials to Prepare*, p. 107.

Classroom Routines

What Time Is It?: Timelines Post the School Day Timeline you made in Session 4.1. Ask students to use the timeline to answer questions about the duration of activities represented on the timeline. With each question students show the beginning and ending times on their small clocks and ask a student volunteer to record the time using digital notation on the board. Some possible questions are:

• How long is Morning Meeting? How long is math class? How long is lunch?

Keep the timeline posted as you will use this timeline for the classroom routines in Sessions 4.3–4.6.

ACTIVITY

① Hours of the Day and Night

20 MIN | CLASS

Direct the students' attention to the large Full Day Timeline, which you made by extending the School Day Timeline from 5 A.M. to 9 P.M. Students should have their completed homework, *Student Activity Book* page 50.

Take a look at this Full Day Timeline. I made it by adding on to the School Day Timeline we made in the last session. Who can help me fill in some of the missing half-hour times? What time should I write here on the timeline?

Ask students to help you fill in times on the half hours. Then ask students about the school day.

At what time does school begin? At what time does it end? Who can show me where school begins on the timeline? Who can show me where it ends? How many hours are we in school?

Ask for examples of events that happen before and after school. Solicit students' responses from their homework. As you discuss each event, write it on the timeline. These events anchor the discussion about time throughout the day.

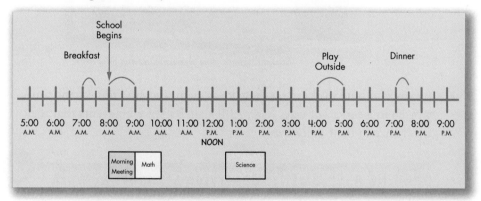

Now focus on events that happen 12 hours apart, to introduce A.M. and P.M.① For example, ask students about events that occur when the clock reads 7:00.

[Amaya] said she eats breakfast at 7 o'clock and [Gregory] said he eats dinner at 7 o'clock. How can that be? . . . [Yama] said one is in the morning and one is at night. . . . Has anyone ever heard of 7 A.M. and 7 P.M.? What part of the day is A.M.? P.M.?

Teaching Note

① **Terminology** A.M. and P.M. stand for *ante meridiem* and *post meridiem* from the Latin for *before noon* and *after noon*. A usage note in the third edition of the *American Heritage Dictionary of the English Language* (p. 77) suggests: "Strictly speaking, 12 A.M. denotes midnight, and 12 P.M. denotes noon, but there is sufficient confusion over these uses to make it advisable to use *12 noon* and *12 midnight* where clarity is required." We also suggest consistently saying *noon* and *midnight* in order to be clear about these times.

Engage students in considering that there are two 12-hour periods in the day. Point out that the hours starting with midnight are labeled *A.M.* and the hours starting with noon are labeled *P.M.*

Where are you at 11 A.M.? . . . What are you doing at 11 P.M.?

Students might say:

"I'm in school at 11 A.M., but I'm in bed at 11 P.M."

Who can show me 11 A.M. on the analog clock? What about 11 P.M.?

Students show a time on a timeline and on a clock.

As you continue working on these ideas, help students connect the times written in a variety of ways (e.g., 7:00 A.M., 8 P.M.) with events that they experience in their daily lives.

ONGOING ASSESSMENT: Observing Students at Work

Students place events on the class's Full Day Timeline.

- **Do students associate times of daily events with appropriate parts of the timeline?**

- **Do students associate times on the analog clock with the corresponding times on the timeline?**

ACTIVITY

② A Timeline for Our Day

40 MIN INDIVIDUALS

Explain to students that they will use Timelines for Morning and Evening Activities (M19) to extend their School Day Timelines to make a Full Day Timeline. They will then mark events from their own lives in the morning or evening on the timeline. Students can work from their homework, *Student Activity Book* page 50. Explain to students that, just as you did for the timeline in the last activity, they should identify times to the whole or half hour.

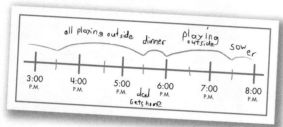

Sample Student Work

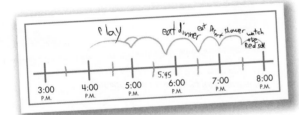

Sample Student Work

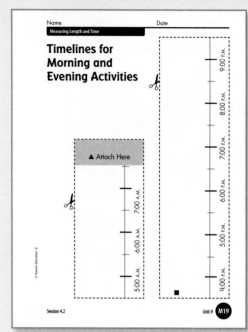

▲ **Resource Masters, M19**

✔ ONGOING ASSESSMENT: Observing Students at Work

Students record events on a timeline using digital notation.

- **Do students glue/tape the timeline so that the times are chronological?**

- **Are students able to use the times from *Student Activity Book* page 50 to fill in the timeline?**

- **Do they mark events on the timeline for appropriate durations?**

As you observe students, ask them questions about the duration of an event.

If you go to an after-school program from 2:30 until 5:00, where should your line start? Where should it end? So, how long does the after-school program last?

How many hours did dinner last? How many half hours is that?

Student Activity Book, p. 51

Name _____ Date _____

Measuring Length and Time

Daily Practice

Number Patterns

Complete the 100 chart.
Look for patterns.

NOTE Students use their knowledge of the counting sequence and patterns to fill in the missing numbers on a 100 chart.
SMH 24

100 Chart

	2	3	4		6	7	8	9	
11		13	14		16	17	18		20
21	22		24		26	27		29	30
31	32	33		36		38	39	40
					47	48	49	50
51	52	53	54					
61	62	63		65			68	69	70
71	72		74	75		77		79	80
81		83	84	85		87	88		90
	92	93	94	95		97	98	99	

Session 4.2 — Unit 9 **51**

▲ **Student Activity Book, p. 51**

Student Activity Book, p. 52

Name _____ Date _____

Measuring Length and Time

Homework

A.M. and P.M.

For each time, write what you are usually doing.

NOTE Students work with the two 12-hour cycles of the 24-hour day.
SMH 142

7:00 A.M. _____

5:00 A.M. _____

12:00 P.M. (noon) _____

7:00 P.M. _____

5:00 P.M. _____

12:00 A.M. (midnight) _____

1. How many hours are there between 12:00 A.M. (midnight) and 12:00 P.M. (noon)? Show how you figured it out.

2. Record the time the first clock shows. Make the second clock show the same time for P.M. and record the time.

 : AM : PM

52 Unit 9 — Session 4.2

▲ **Student Activity Book, p. 52**

DIFFERENTIATION: Supporting the Range of Learners

Intervention For students having difficulty showing events from their homework on the timeline, ask them to first show the beginning and ending times on the analog clock and then to locate the beginning and ending times on the timeline. Since students are familiar with the analog clock from the *What Time Is It?* routines throughout the year, use this representation to ground the concept of representing time on a timeline.

Making their own timelines helps students see how times can be represented horizontally.

SESSION FOLLOW-UP

3 Daily Practice and Homework

Daily Practice: For ongoing review, have students complete *Student Activity Book* page 51.

Homework: For homework, students work on *Student Activity Book* page 52. They write what they did during the day at a certain time in the A.M. and the equivalent time in the P.M. Students may need to check with parents about what they do at certain times of the day.

Student Math Handbook: Students and families may use *Student Math Handbook* pages 142, 143, 144, 145 for reference and review. See pages 172–178 in the back of this unit.

Fred & Winnipeg Timelines

Math Focus Points

◆ Moving forward and backward along a timeline in multiples of hours and half hours

◆ Connecting a time, its digital notation, and its representation on an analog clock to a timeline

◆ Using a timeline to determine duration

Today's Plan		Materials
ACTIVITY **① Daily Schedule: Fred & Winnipeg**	50 MIN CLASS INDIVIDUALS	• *Student Activity Book*, pp. 53–60 • T87 📄; T88 📄; M22*; M23* (as needed); M24* (optional); M25* (optional) • Student clocks (as needed)
DISCUSSION **② Calculating Duration**	10 MIN CLASS	• T88 📄 (from Activity 1) • Demonstration clock
SESSION FOLLOW-UP **③ Daily Practice**		• *Student Activity Book*, p. 61 • *Student Math Handbook*, pp. 142, 143, 144, 145

*See *Materials to Prepare*, p. 107.

Classroom Routines

What Time Is It?: Timelines Ask students to use the School Day Timeline to answer the following questions:

Math starts an hour *after* morning meeting begins. When does math start? Math ends two hours *before* lunch begins. When does math end?

We go to gym half an hour *before* we go home. When does gym begin?

Science class begins an hour *after* math ends. When does science start?

With each question students show the beginning and ending times on their small clocks and ask a student volunteer to record the time using digital notation on the board.

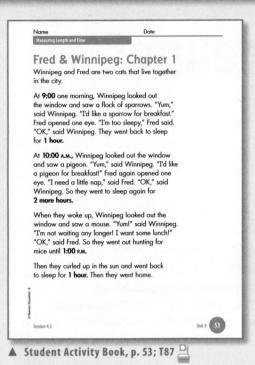

▲ Student Activity Book, p. 53; T87

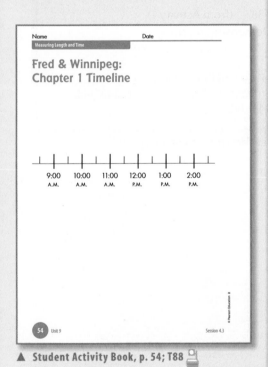

▲ Student Activity Book, p. 54; T88

50 MIN   CLASS   INDIVIDUALS

ACTIVITY

① Daily Schedule: Fred & Winnipeg

Display the transparency of Fred & Winnipeg: Chapter 1 (T87) and read the story aloud with the class. After reading through the story once, begin making a vertical schedule of the events in Chapter 1 on the board.

Let's make a list of what happens in the story. What happens first? What time does Winnipeg see sparrows? Then what happens?

Record each time span and the corresponding activity.

> 9:00 A.M. Winnipeg sees sparrows
>
> 9:00 A.M.–10:00 A.M. Sleep
>
> 10:00 A.M. Winnipeg sees a pigeon
>
> 10:00 A.M.–12:00 P.M. Sleep for 2 hours
>
> 12:00 P.M.–1:00 P.M. Hunting
>
> 1:00 P.M.–2:00 P.M. Sleep in the sun

Show the overhead transparency of Fred & Winnipeg: Chapter 1 Timeline (T88).

Let's fill in the timeline with events from the story. First, Winnipeg sees sparrows. Where does that go on the timeline? How can I show that? For how long do the cats sleep?

As a class, continue until you have filled in all of the events of Chapter 1 on the timeline.

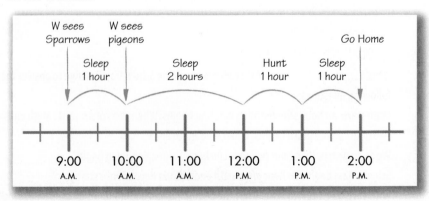

Then give students copies of Fred & Winnipeg: Chapter 2 (M22 or *Student Activity Book* page 55).

Here's a new day of Fred and Winnipeg's adventures. Read through the story. Then fill out the timeline on *Student Activity Book* page 57.

ONGOING ASSESSMENT: Observing Students at Work

Students record events on a timeline. As you observe students, ask them questions about the duration of the events.

- **Do students mark events on the timeline for appropriate durations?**

- **Do students treat each mark on the timeline as representing a point in time?**

- **Do students use the timeline to figure out the duration of an event?**

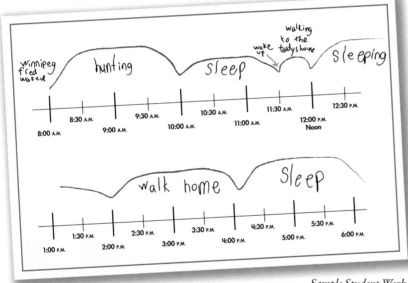

Sample Student Work

DIFFERENTIATION: Supporting the Range of Learners

Intervention Students who need help with the structure of the story can fill out Fred & Winnipeg: Chapter 2 List of Events (M23 or *Student Activity Book* page 56) before they write the events on the timeline.

Intervention Some students may write each event at a single time instead of showing the duration of the event. Ask them to show the beginning and ending time of an event on their clocks, then help them mark those two times on the timeline, and connect them with a curve.

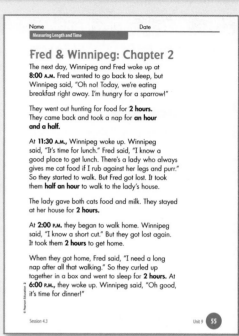

Name _____ Date _____
Measuring Length and Time

Fred & Winnipeg: Chapter 2

The next day, Winnipeg and Fred woke up at **8:00 A.M.** Fred wanted to go back to sleep, but Winnipeg said, "Oh no! Today, we're eating breakfast right away. I'm hungry for a sparrow!"

They went out hunting for food for **2 hours.** They came back and took a nap for **an hour and a half.**

At **11:30 A.M.,** Winnipeg woke up. Winnipeg said, "It's time for lunch." Fred said, "I know a good place to get lunch. There's a lady who always gives me cat food if I rub against her legs and purr." So they started to walk. But Fred got lost. It took them **half an hour** to walk to the lady's house.

The lady gave both cats food and milk. They stayed at her house for **2 hours.**

At **2:00 P.M.** they began to walk home. Winnipeg said, "I know a short cut." But they got lost again. It took them **2 hours** to get home.

When they got home, Fred said, "I need a long nap after all that walking." So they curled up together in a box and went to sleep for **2 hours.** At **6:00 P.M.,** they woke up. Winnipeg said, "Oh good, it's time for dinner!"

Session 4.3 — Unit 9 **55**

▲ **Student Activity Book, p. 55; Resource Masters, M22**

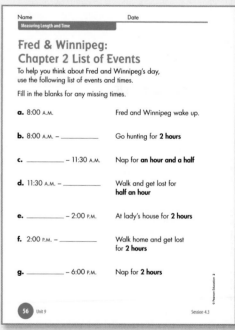

Name _____ Date _____
Measuring Length and Time

Fred & Winnipeg: Chapter 2 List of Events

To help you think about Fred and Winnipeg's day, use the following list of events and times.

Fill in the blanks for any missing times.

a. 8:00 A.M.   Fred and Winnipeg wake up.

b. 8:00 A.M. – _____   Go hunting for **2 hours**

c. _____ – 11:30 A.M.   Nap for **an hour and a half**

d. 11:30 A.M. – _____   Walk and get lost for **half an hour**

e. _____ – 2:00 P.M.   At lady's house for **2 hours**

f. 2:00 P.M. – _____   Walk home and get lost for **2 hours**

g. _____ – 6:00 P.M.   Nap for **2 hours**

56 Unit 9   Session 4.3

▲ **Student Activity Book, p. 56; Resource Masters, M23**

Professional Development

❶ **Dialogue Box:** Not Even a Second Has Gone By: Calculating Duration, p. 170

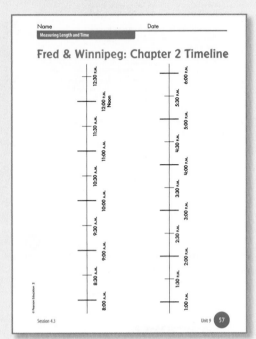

▲ Student Activity Book, p. 57

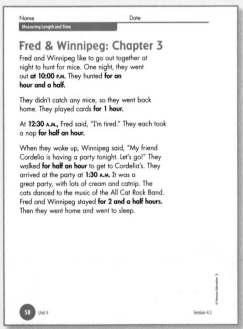

▲ Student Activity Book, p. 58; Resource Masters, M24

Extension Students who complete Chapter 2 can go on to Chapter 3 using copies of Fred & Winnipeg: Chapter 3 (M24–M25) or *Student Activity Book* pages 58–60.

DISCUSSION

2 Calculating Duration

10 MIN   CLASS

Math Focus Points for Discussion

◆ Moving forward and backward along a timeline in multiples of hours and half hours

◆ Using a timeline to determine duration

Display the transparency of Fred & Winnipeg: Chapter 1 Timeline (T88) that you filled in during the earlier activity.

Ask students to think about the duration of combinations of events on the timeline by asking questions about the duration of multiple events.❶

How long is it from the time Winnipeg sees sparrows until the time she sees a pigeon?

Fred and Winnipeg napped at 10:00 A.M. for 2 hours. After that, they hunted for an hour. How long was it from when they started to nap to when they finished hunting? Who can show us how you're thinking about this on the timeline? Who can show us how you're thinking about this on an analog clock?

A student uses a timeline to calculate duration of time.

Continue to ask questions about the duration of different events on the timeline. After each question, ask students to show their ideas on the timeline and on the clock.

What time did Winnipeg see sparrows? Who can show this on the analog clock? How long was it from the time she saw the sparrows until they went hunting?

SESSION FOLLOW-UP

3 Daily Practice

Daily Practice: For reinforcement of this unit's content, have students complete *Student Activity Book* page 61.

Student Math Handbook: Students and families may use *Student Math Handbook* pages 142, 143, 144, 145 for reference and review. See pages 172–178 in the back of this unit.

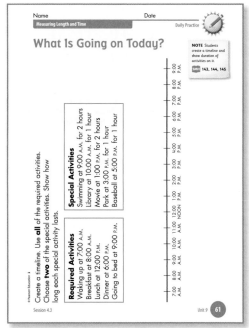

▲ **Student Activity Book, p. 61**

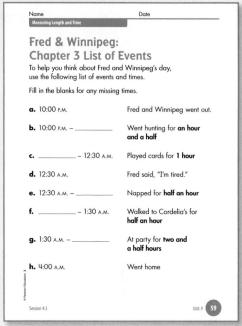

▲ **Student Activity Book, p. 59; Resource Masters, M25**

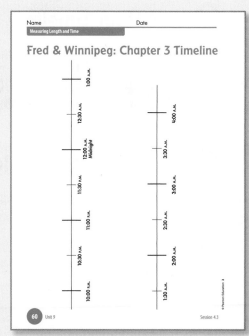

▲ **Student Activity Book, p. 60**

Solving Timeline Problems

Math Focus Points

◆ Moving forward and backward along a timeline in multiples of hours, half hours, and quarter hours

◆ Connecting a time, its digital notation, and its representation on an analog clock to a timeline

◆ Using a timeline to determine duration

◆ Using a timeline to show a 24-hour period

Today's Plan		Materials
ACTIVITY **① How Long Is It? Quarter Hours**	 10 MIN CLASS	• T89 • Demonstration clocks; Student clocks (as needed)
ACTIVITY **② A 24-Hour Timeline**	 15 MIN CLASS PAIRS	• Full Day Timeline (from Session 4.2); chart paper
ACTIVITY **③ Daily Schedules: Fred & Winnipeg Timeline Problems**	 35 MIN PAIRS	• *Student Activity Book,* pp. 62–63 • M27–M28*
SESSION FOLLOW-UP **④ Daily Practice and Homework**		• *Student Activity Book,* pp. 64–65 • *Student Math Handbook,* pp. 136, 137–138, 139, 140, 142, 143, 144, 145

*See *Materials to Prepare,* p. 107.

Classroom Routines

What Time Is It?: Timelines Students use the School Day Timeline of the daily schedule to pose questions for the class about duration of time. This is modeled after the routine they have been doing for the previous two sessions.

ACTIVITY
1 How Long Is It? Quarter Hours

10 MIN CLASS

Display the transparency of How Long Is It? Quarter Hours (T89). Underneath the timeline write a few major events of the school day. Above the timeline use curved lines to show the duration of two or three events involving quarter hours. Include at least one event that starts or ends at 15 minutes before the hour and an event that starts or ends 15 minutes after the hour.❶ (If the real events for the day don't allow this, ask students to imagine that they do.) Label the events but do not write in the digital times for quarter hours.

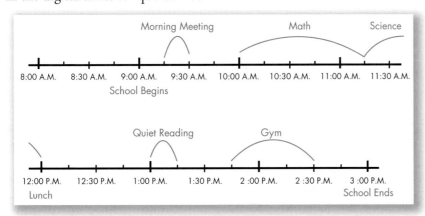

Focusing on one of these events, ask students about beginning and ending times. If students have difficulty naming the times which involve quarter hours, ask them to describe when it falls with respect to known times to establish that each quarter hour is 15 minutes, and that 2 quarter hours are 30 minutes.

At what time does [Morning Meeting] start? If you're not sure what time this is, can you describe what time comes before or after it?

Students might say:

"It's between 9:00 and 9:30."

"Morning Meeting begins after 9:00 A.M. and before 9:30 A.M."

"It falls in between the two times."

Teaching Note
❶ **Quarter Hours** Students were introduced to quarter hours during Grade 2 Fraction Unit and in the Classroom Routine *What Time Is It?* Refer back to those activities if students need a review and practice of quarter hours.

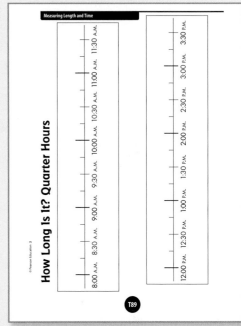

▲ **Transparencies, T89**

Ask students how many minutes pass from [9:00 to 9:30].

Can someone show me on the analog clock the area between [9:00 and 9:30]? How many minutes pass from [9:00 to 9:30]? What would the time be that is halfway between [9:00 and 9:30]?

[Melissa] is showing us [9:15] on the analog clock, and [Luis] says that on the timeline the mark in the middle of [9:00 and 9:30] must also be [9:15]. How many minutes are there from [9:15 to 9:30]?

If we look at the area between [9:00 and 9:15], what do you notice? [Nadia] says it is one fourth and [Lonzell] says it is one quarter, that's why 15 minutes is also called a quarter hour.

Continue to ask questions about the duration of events on the timeline, including events that start or end at 15 minutes before or after the hour. As students discuss an event, write the digital time for that event on the timeline. Save this transparency with the events and times you've recorded for use in the next session.

ONGOING ASSESSMENT: Observing Students at Work

Students interpret a timeline that shows events in a school day, including events that start or end on the quarter hour.

- **Do students associate times that are 15 minutes before or after the hour with locations on the timeline?**

- **Do students think about an hour as being comprised of 4 quarter hours?**

- **Can students calculate duration using the timeline?**

DIFFERENTIATION: Supporting the Range of Learners

Intervention For students having difficulty with the meaning of a quarter hour, indicate an interval of one full hour on the timeline that begins and ends on the hour, for example, from 1:00 to 2:00. Ask them to show 1:00 and 2:00 on their analog clocks, and then ask about half hours and quarter hours.

- How many minutes pass between 1:00 and 2:00? How many minutes is that? How many half hours are there in an hour? How many minutes in each half hour?

- What is the time half an hour after 1:00? Show it on the analog clock. Where is that on the timeline?

- What if we divide an hour into 4 quarter hours? How many minutes is each quarter hour?

- What is the time 15 minutes after 1:00? Show it on the analog clock. Where is that on the timeline?

As the Investigation continues, ask students to find times on the analog clock and on the timeline in order to make connections between the two representations.

ACTIVITY

2 A 24-Hour Timeline

15 MIN   CLASS   PAIRS

Call students' attention to the posted Full Day Timeline which you have been using during the previous sessions. Ask students about extending it forward to midnight.

This timeline goes from 6:00 A.M. to 10:00 P.M. What comes after ten o'clock? How many more hours is it until midnight?

Ask students to talk in pairs about this for a minute or two. Then ask them to tell you how to extend the timeline. Extend the timeline and write the digital notation for 10:30 P.M., 11:00 P.M., 11:30 P.M., and 12:00 A.M. (midnight).

What if I wanted to go backward from 6:00 A.M.? How far would I have to go to get to midnight?

Again ask students to talk together briefly, and then have them share their ideas with the class. Encourage students to share their ideas even if they do not have a complete solution. Follow up with questions about going back one hour at a time from 6:00 A.M.

What if I went one hour back from 6:00 A.M.? What time would it be?

Once the timeline is completed from midnight to midnight, ask students to talk about what it looks like outside and what people might be doing at midnight and at noon. Remind students that there are 2 periods of 12 hours in each day and we distinguish these by calling the hours starting with midnight A.M. and the hours starting with noon P.M.

How many hours does this timeline show from midnight to noon? What about from noon to midnight? When are the hours that we are usually awake? What about the hours we are usually sleeping?

It may help your students if you extend the timeline even further from midnight to the time students might be getting up the next day, so students can see a complete night and day.

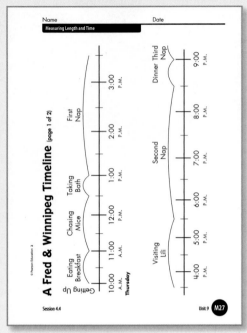

▲ Resource Masters, M27

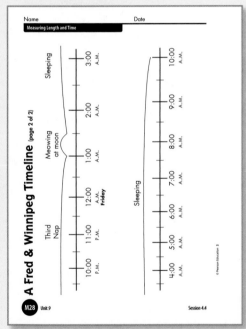

▲ Resource Masters, M28

So, this timeline from midnight to midnight shows us today, [Thursday]. If we go past midnight until tomorrow, what day will that be? What if we go in the other direction? Which way would we go on the timeline to get to yesterday?

Point to a few points on the timeline that students may not usually think about and ask them to imagine what might be going on then. Keep in mind your own students' experiences and what they may know about in their own lives and environments that happens during the night as you pose your questions. Some examples are:

- Does anyone in your family have to be at work very early, even before you go to school?

- Are there certain chores someone in your family does before you get up? What time do you think that person has to get up?

- Do you know someone who works at night? A nurse sometimes works during the night. What time might that person go to work? Come home?

Also, ask questions about the names of times.

If I said 1 P.M., what time of the day would it be? Would you be awake or asleep? If I said 1 A.M., what part of the day would it be? Would you be awake or asleep?

End the discussion by focusing on the 24-hour period, asking what would happen if you kept extending the timeline to the right. Students may respond that the times "keep repeating" or that the two 12-hour cycles begin again.

Keep this timeline posted as students will add events to it in the following session.

ONGOING ASSESSMENT: Observing Students at Work

Students extend the Full Day Timeline in both directions so that it represents 24 hours, from midnight to midnight. They discuss what happens in people's lives during times designated by A.M. and P.M.

- **Do students understand the meaning and sequence of times as they extend the timeline in both directions?**

- **Can students associate appropriate activities with different times of day?** Do they distinguish what time of day is represented by, for example, 1 P.M. and 1 A.M.?

Using a timeline gives students a visual representation of a 24-hour day. With it the student can identify the difference between times that are numbered the same way, such as 1:00 A.M. and 1:00 P.M.

ACTIVITY

35 MIN   PAIRS

3 Daily Schedules: Fred & Winnipeg Timeline Problems

Distribute copies of A Fred & Winnipeg Timeline (M27–M28) to students. Students use the timeline to answer questions on *Student Activity Book* pages 62–63. Unlike activities thus far, this activity presents a completed timeline for students to interpret.

Before they begin work, orient students to the timeline with a few questions that focus on the units of the timeline and how the timeline shows duration.

What **intervals** does this timeline use?

For how long did Fred and Winnipeg eat breakfast? How would you write this?

Solicit students' ideas on how to write the duration of an event. If someone suggests writing the duration as 1:00, ask questions to help students see that this is not the correct notation.

If I write 1:00 for how long they ate breakfast, does that mean they ate for one hour? Does it mean they ate at one o'clock? What does the timeline show? How can we write the **duration** without it looking like we're writing the time of day?

Name _____ Date _____

Measuring Length and Time

Fred & Winnipeg Timeline Problems (page 1 of 2)

Look at the timeline.

How long did each activity take?

Activity	Begins	Ends	How long did it take?
Eating Breakfast	10:00	11:00	1 hour
Chasing Mice			
Taking Bath			
First Nap			
Visiting Lili			
Second Nap			
Eating Dinner			
Third Nap			
Meowing at Moon			
Sleeping			

62   Unit 9   Session 4.4

▲ **Student Activity Book, p. 62**

Name _____ Date _____

Measuring Length and Time

Fred & Winnipeg Timeline Problems (page 2 of 2)

1. After breakfast, Fred said, "How long until dinner?" How long did Fred have to wait for dinner? _____

   How did you figure it out? _____
   _____
   _____

2. When they got up, Winnipeg said, "I wonder when Lili will get here?" How long did Winnipeg have to wait for Lili? _____

   How did you figure it out? _____
   _____
   _____

3. How long did Fred and Winnipeg sleep? Include all of the times they were asleep or napping. _____

   How did you figure it out? _____
   _____
   _____

Session 4.4   Unit 9   63

▲ **Student Activity Book, p. 63**

Refer to students' own experience when talking about the duration of events:

How would you tell me how long you were reading if you started reading at 2:00 and stopped at 4:00? [Carla] just said, "I was reading for 2 hours." How would you write the length of time just the way [Carla] said it?

If students do not suggest it, show them how to write one hour's duration as *1 hour, 1 h, 1 hr,* or *60 minutes.*

ONGOING ASSESSMENT: Observing Students at Work

Students calculate the duration of events by reading a timeline.

- **Can students determine the length of an interval of time using the timeline?**

- **Can students read an event on the timeline that ends on one line segment of the timeline and begins on the segment below, such as "Visiting Lili"?**

DIFFERENTIATION: Supporting the Range of Learners

Intervention Students may have difficulty counting the number of hours on the timeline when the duration includes the interval from 12:00 to 1:00. For example, Fred and Winnipeg's third nap begins at 9:00 P.M. and continues until 1:00 A.M. Provide students with questions to help calculate the 4-hour duration by breaking it into 2 parts.

How many hours is it from 9:00 P.M. until 12:00 midnight? How many more hours is it from 12:00 midnight until 1:00 A.M.?

Some questions require that students add whole numbers and fractions. Students having difficulty adding these can first combine the total number of hours, then the total number of half hours, and then add these 2 values together.

> 3. How long did Fred and Winnipeg sleep? Include all of the times they were asleep or napping. _18 hours_
>
> How did you figure it out? _I counted hours by hours and then I started countering half hours. (Then it got hard.) That is how I got my answer_

Sample Student Work

3. How long did Fred and Winnipeg sleep? Include all of the times they were asleep or napping. __18 hours__

How did you figure it out? _____

$$2 + 3 + 4 + 8 = 17$$
$$\tfrac{1}{2} + \tfrac{1}{2} = 1 \text{ hour}$$
$$17 + 1 = \boxed{18}$$

Sample Student Work

SESSION FOLLOW-UP

4 Daily Practice and Homework

 Daily Practice: For reinforcement of this unit's content, have students complete *Student Activity Book* page 64.

 Homework: Explain to students that during the next lesson they will design a timeline for their own Special Day. For homework, they will work on *Student Activity Book* page 65. It is a writing assignment to think up some special activities they would like to do for each time of the day—morning, afternoon, and night—on their Special Day.

 Student Math Handbook: Students and families may use *Student Math Handbook* pages 136, 137–138, 139, 140, 142, 143, 144, 145 for reference and review. See pages 172–178 in the back of this unit.

▲ Student Activity Book, p. 64

▲ Student Activity Book, p. 65

Special Day Timelines

Math Focus Points

◆ Moving forward and backward along a timeline in multiples of hours, half hours, and quarter hours

◆ Using a timeline to determine duration

◆ Using a timeline to show a 24-hour period

◆ Recording events on a timeline

Today's Plan		Materials
ACTIVITY **① How Long Is It? Quarter Hours**	15 MIN CLASS	• T89 (from Session 4.4)
ACTIVITY **② Introducing Special Day Timelines**	10 MIN CLASS	• *Student Activity Book*, p. 65 (from Session 4.4) • 24-Hour Timeline (from Session 4.3); student clocks
ACTIVITY **③ Special Day Timelines**	35 MIN INDIVIDUALS	• M29–M30* • Scissors; glue or tape
SESSION FOLLOW-UP **④ Daily Practice**		• *Student Activity Book*, p. 67 • *Student Math Handbook*, pp. 136, 137–138, 139, 140, 142, 143, 144, 145

*See *Materials to Prepare*, p. 109.

Classroom Routines

What Time Is It?: Timelines Ask students to use the School Day Timeline of the daily schedule that was extended in the previous session to include the beginning and ending of the day, to answer the following questions:

• If it is [6:30 P.M.], and you [go to bed] in [one and one-half hours] what time will you [go to bed]?

Ask a variety of these types of questions as students point out the interval on the timeline and also set their clocks to the correct times.

15 MIN   CLASS

ACTIVITY

How Long Is It? Quarter Hours

Display the transparency of How Long Is It? Quarter Hours (T89), which was used in the previous session and is labeled with your school day schedule. Continue to ask questions about duration using this timeline. You may also want to review the use of A.M. and P.M. noting this on the timeline. Add more events, incorporating times beginning and ending on the half hour and quarter hour. Over the course of this activity, choose from the following four kinds of problem questions:

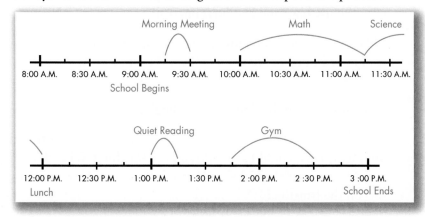

1. How long is [gym]?

2. How long is it from [the beginning of math] until [the end of school]?

3. If it is [1:15 p.m.] and we are going to [gym] in [1 hour], when will we [go to gym]?

4. If it is [12:30 p.m.] and I have been eating lunch for [half an hour], when did I start [to eat lunch]? How many minutes is that?

ONGOING ASSESSMENT: Observing Students at Work

Students interpret a timeline that shows events in a school day and solve problems about duration.

- **Do students associate times that are 15 minutes before or after the hour with locations on the timeline?**

- **Do students connect times on the analog clock with the timeline?**

- **Can students calculate duration using the timeline?**

ACTIVITY

2 Introducing Special Day Timelines

10 MIN   CLASS

Post or draw attention to the 24-hour timeline created in Session 4.4. Point to an hour mark and ask students to show the time on their small analog clocks.

Introduce students to the Special Day Timeline by talking about what special activities might be in your day.

Begin to tell students a story of what might be a special day for you, using mostly hour and half-hour intervals.

I like to sleep late, so on my special day, I'll get up at 11:00 A.M. and read in bed until 12:00 noon. Then I'll eat lunch. At 12:30 P.M., I'll exercise.

Draw attention to the times after midnight.

We all have different bedtimes. On my special day, I went to bed at midnight. How could I show this on the timeline? What does that look like on your clock? I slept through the night. How could I show this on the timeline?

Then indicate what students will do to make their own timeline for a special day.

Today you're going to start creating your own timelines for a special day. This special day will include activities you listed for homework on *Student Activity Book* page 65. In addition to what you listed, we will agree on some required activities that you will include on your Special Day Timelines.

Make a list on the board with your students of required activities. Write the heading, "Required Activities." Ask students to name some activities that might be common to everyone. These might include waking up, breakfast, lunch, dinner, and bedtime.

Required Activities	Special Activities
waking up	going to a ball game
breakfast	going to the movies
lunch	playing basketball
dinner	taking a hike
bedtime	going on a picnic
	going swimming

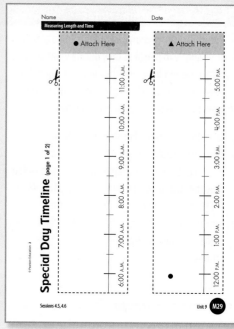

▲ **Resource Masters, M29**

Now I'd like to hear some of the activities you thought about that you'd like to have on your special days. We'll list some of them just to give everyone ideas.

Make a list of "Special Activities." Ask students for activities they thought about for the morning, afternoon, evening, and night. As students work on their Special Day Timelines, they can choose activities from the class list or use ideas of their own that they generated for homework.

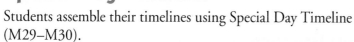

ACTIVITY

35 MIN INDIVIDUALS

③ Special Day Timelines

Students assemble their timelines using Special Day Timeline (M29–M30).

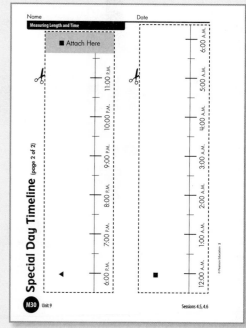

▲ **Resource Masters, M30**

Assembling a 24-hour timeline gives students an opportunity to think about the sequence of hours and events over a whole day and night.

Teaching Notes

❶ **Rough Draft** Encourage students to do a rough draft lightly in pencil as they decide what activities to include and how long they will last. Then they can go over them with crayons or markers and draw pictures to illustrate the activities.

❷ **Class Preparation** For students who may have difficulty cutting and preparing their own Special Day Timeline, prepare ahead of time a few timelines using Special Day Timeline (M29–M30). For students requiring more room on their timelines to write in events, make enlarged copies of the timeline. Enlarge the timeline to 30% and print on $8\frac{1}{2}''$ x 14″ paper.

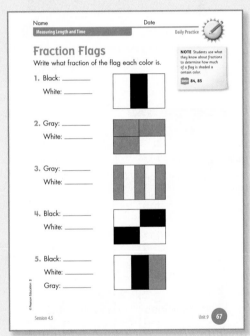

▲ **Student Activity Book, p. 67**

Students must use all of the activities on your "Required Activities" list. Then they should choose some special activities to put on their timelines. They must mark where each activity begins and ends, and draw lines to show how long each activity lasts.❶

ONGOING ASSESSMENT: Observing Students at Work

This activity offers opportunities for students to write events on a 24-hour timeline.❷

- **Can students plan their day with reasonable lengths of time for the activities they choose?**

- **Are students able to choose the duration they want for an activity and show that duration accurately on the timeline?**

- **Do students know which times on the 24-hour timeline are morning, afternoon, evening, and night?**

DIFFERENTIATION: Supporting the Range of Learners

(**Intervention**) Some students may benefit from working with you in a small group as they make their timeline. Also, it may be appropriate for some students to work only in intervals that begin on the hour or half hour.

SESSION FOLLOW-UP

4 Daily Practice

 Daily Practice: For ongoing review, have students complete *Student Activity Book* page 67.

 Student Math Handbook: Students and families may use *Student Math Handbook* pages 136, 137–138, 139, 140, 142, 143, 144, 145, for reference and review. See pages 172–178 in the back of this unit.

Comparing Special Day Timelines

Math Focus Points

◆ Connecting a time, its digital notation, and its representation on an analog clock to a timeline

◆ Using a timeline to determine duration

◆ Naming and using notation for times that are 30 and 15 minutes before or after the hour

Today's Plan			Materials
ACTIVITY **① How Long Is It?** **Maria's Timeline**	🕐 **15 MIN**	👥 **CLASS**	• T90 • Demonstration clock
ACTIVITY **② Special Day Timelines**	🕐 **30 MIN**	👤 **INDIVIDUALS**	• *Student Activity Book*, pp. 65 (from Session 4.4) and 68 (optional) • Special Day Timeline (from Session 4.5)
DISCUSSION **③ Comparing Special Day Timelines**	🕐 **15 MIN**	👥 **CLASS**	• *Student Activity Book*, p. 68 • Demonstration clock
SESSION FOLLOW-UP **④ Daily Practice**			• *Student Activity Book*, p. 69 • *Student Math Handbook*, pp. 143, 144, 145

Classroom Routines

What Time Is It?: Timelines Ask students to use the School Day Timeline of the extended daily schedule to answer the following types of questions:

• If it is [4 P.M.], and I've [played outside] for [an hour and a half] when did I start [to play outside]? How many hours is that? If it is [8 A.M.], and I have [been awake] for [2 hours] what time did I wake up? How many half hours is that?

Ask a variety of these types of questions as students point out the interval on the timeline and also set their clocks to the correct times.

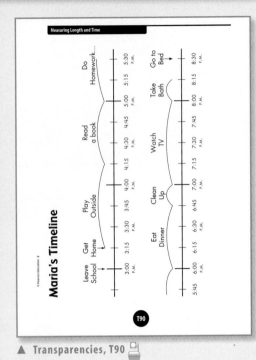

Maria's Timeline

Measuring Length and Time

| Leave School | Get Home | Play Outside | | Read a book | | Do Homework... |
| 3:00 P.M. | 3:15 P.M. | 3:30 P.M. | 3:45 P.M. | 4:00 P.M. | 4:15 P.M. | 4:30 P.M. | 4:45 P.M. | 5:00 P.M. | 5:15 P.M. | 5:30 P.M. |

| Eat Dinner | | Clean Up | | Watch TV | | Take Bath | | Go to Bed |
| 5:45 P.M. | 6:00 P.M. | 6:15 P.M. | 6:30 P.M. | 6:45 P.M. | 7:00 P.M. | 7:15 P.M. | 7:30 P.M. | 7:45 P.M. | 8:00 P.M. | 8:15 P.M. | 8:30 P.M. |

T90

▲ Transparencies, T90

ACTIVITY

1 How Long Is It? Maria's Timeline

15 MIN   CLASS

Math Focus Points for Discussion

◆ Naming and using notation for times that are 30 and 15 minutes before or after the hour

Show the transparency of Maria's Timeline (T90).

Here's a timeline of what a second grader, Maria, did after school one day. What can you tell me about what she did by looking at the timeline?

After students have described the timeline, ask questions about duration, focusing on the activities that start or end at 15 minutes before or after the hour. For students who continue to work through ideas of half hour, focus on activities that start or end on the half hour. For example,

How long did it take Maria to get home from school? How long did she watch TV? For how long did she take a bath?

Ask students to explain how they figured out the duration of the activity and to show how they know, using the timeline and the analog clock.

ACTIVITY

2 Special Day Timelines

30 MIN   INDIVIDUALS

Students finish work on their Special Day Timelines (from Session 4.5). If students have most of their Special Day Timelines to complete, encourage them to first complete the "Required Activities," and then move on to the "Special Activities" from their homework, *Student Activity Book* page 65.

As students complete their timelines, post them in the display area you have prepared for this purpose. Select five or six examples to use during the final discussion to exemplify times for required events, a variety of durations, or original activities.

Students who finish can work on *Student Activity Book* page 68. They can look at the Special Day Timelines that have been posted and also walk around the room to look at any timelines being completed as they work on this page.

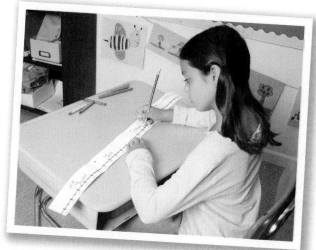

A student shows events on the Special Day Timeline.

ONGOING ASSESSMENT: Observing Students at Work

Students complete their own timelines, then read and interpret other students' timelines.

- **Can students read and interpret other students' timelines?**

- **Can students determine durations of activities on the timelines?**

DISCUSSION

3 Comparing Special Day Timelines

15 MIN CLASS

Math Focus Points for Discussion

◆ Using a timeline to determine duration

Focus this discussion on some of the questions on *Student Activity Book* page 68. It is not necessary for all students to have completed this page. ❶

Who thinks they might have gotten up earliest on their Special Day? What time did you get up? Who thinks they might have done one activity the longest? What was it? What time did it start and end?

What was your favorite activity on your own timeline? When did it start and when did it end? Who can figure out how long that was?

Differentiation

❶ **English Language Learners** The large amount of vocabulary embedded in these questions might make it hard for English Language Learners to participate in this discussion. You can preview this discussion with a small group of English Language Learners, using their own timelines for reference. Ask similar types of questions and clarify key vocabulary. (See English Language Learners Overview on page 18.) Then encourage students to ask questions about each other's timelines.

Name _____ Date _____

Measuring Length and Time

Comparing Special Day Timelines

Use the Special Day Timelines from our class to answer these questions.

1. Who got up the earliest? _____

   What time? _____

2. Who woke up the latest? _____

   What time? _____

3. Who did one activity
   for a very long time? _____

   What was the activity? _____

   How long was it? _____

4. Who did something for exactly
   1 hour and a half?

   Who did it? _____

   What was the activity? _____

   What time did it start? _____

   What time did it end? _____

68 Unit 9   Session 4.6

▲ **Student Activity Book, p. 68**

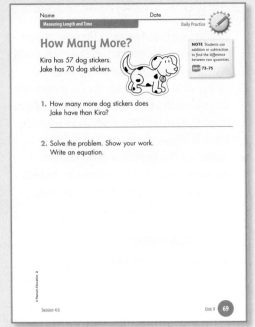

▲ **Student Activity Book, p. 69**

Focus the next part of the discussion on the 5 or 6 timelines you have chosen and ask questions that compare the events.

I am thinking of a Special Day Timeline that shows someone [at the beach for 3 hours]. Who can find the one I'm thinking of? How do you know that it shows [3 hours at the beach]? Who can show me the starting and ending times on the analog clock? How can you tell this is three hours on the analog clock?

I am thinking of a timeline that shows someone spent [an hour and a half playing baseball]. Who can find the one I'm thinking of? How do you know that it shows [an hour and a half of playing baseball]? Who can show me how you know it is an [hour and a half] by using the analog clock?

Students can then compare the times and duration of events among the posted timelines.

Here are [4] of your timelines. Who ate dinner the latest? Who woke up the earliest? Who had the longest lunch? How do you know?

SESSION FOLLOW-UP

4 Daily Practice

Daily Practice: For ongoing review, have students complete *Student Activity Book* page 69.

Student Math Handbook: Students and families may use *Student Math Handbook* pages 143, 144, 145 for reference and review. See pages 172–178 in the back of this unit.

End-of-Unit Assessment

Math Focus Points

◆ Understanding that different-sized units yield different counts (the smaller the unit, the higher the count)

◆ Using inches and centimeters to describe lengths

◆ Measuring lengths that are longer than 12 inches

◆ Using a timeline to determine duration

Today's Plan		Materials
ASSESSMENT ACTIVITY **❶ End-of-Unit Assessment**	✓ 🕐 🧍 **60 MIN INDIVIDUALS**	• M32*; M33–M34*; M35* • Rulers (1 per student); strips of adding machine tape* (1 per student)
SESSION FOLLOW-UP **❷ Daily Practice**		• *Student Activity Book,* p. 70 • *Student Math Handbook,* pp. 144, 145, 155, 156

*See *Materials to Prepare,* p. 109.

Classroom Routines

What Time Is It?: Timelines Ask students to use the School Day Timeline of the extended daily schedule to answer the following types of questions:

• If it is [7:30 P.M.], and I've been [eating dinner] for [an hour and a half] when did I start [to eat dinner]? How many half hours is that? If it is [11:30 A.M.], and I [brushed my teeth] [2 and a half hours] ago what time did I [brush my teeth]? How many half hours is that?

Ask a variety of these types of questions as students point out the interval on the timeline and also set their clocks to the correct times.

Math Note

❶ Actual Lengths The line is 13 centimeters and approximately $5\frac{1}{4}$ inches long.

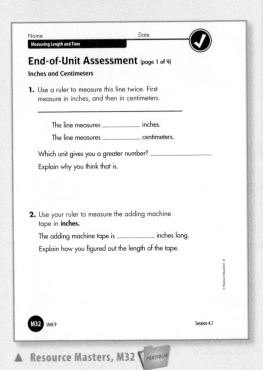

▲ Resource Masters, M32 [PORTFOLIO]

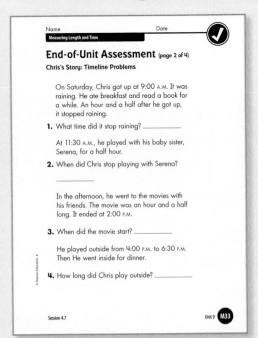

▲ Resource Masters, M33 [PORTFOLIO]

ASSESSMENT ACTIVITY
❶ End-of-Unit Assessment

60 MIN INDIVIDUALS

Let students know that today they will be solving some problems about measuring length and working with timelines. Explain that they will work individually so that you can get a sense of how their strategies and ideas have developed since the beginning of this unit. The purpose of the assessment is to see how students work with the math ideas of this unit, so provide whatever support is needed to be sure that the students understand the directions.

The first assessment problem—Inches and Centimeters (M32)—has two main problems. It addresses Benchmark 4: Measure objects using inches and centimeters and Benchmark 5: Use a ruler to measure lengths longer than a foot. The first task is to measure a line in inches and in centimeters, identify which measurement has the larger number, and explain why. The second task is to measure a strip of adding machine tape that is 17 inches long (longer than the ruler). Students are to explain how they calculated their answer.❶

In the second assessment problem, Chris's Story: Timeline Problems, (M33–M34) students use information from Chris's day to determine duration of events and then show these events on Chris's Story: Timeline (M35). It addresses Benchmark 6: Solve problems involving the beginning time of an event, ending time of an event, and duration of the event; given two of these, find the third for events beginning and ending on the hour or half hour and Benchmark 7: Use a timeline to record and determine duration to the hour or half hour.

Do as much observation and note-taking as you can as students are engaged in the assessment. Their written work will provide some information, but you will gain more information through observing how they work.❷

ONGOING ASSESSMENT: Observing Students at Work

Students solve problems about measuring lengths and timelines.

- **Are students able to measure accurately with the ruler?**

- **Do students recognize that there are more centimeters in the measure because a centimeter is a smaller unit of measure than an inch?**

- **Are students able to accurately measure a length longer than a 12-inch ruler?**

- **Can students determine the length of an interval of time using the timeline?**

- **Can students write an hour or half-hour time in digital notation?**

If you have some time at the end of the session, after students have finished, choose one of the problems to talk about in a class discussion.

SESSION FOLLOW-UP
2 Daily Practice

 Daily Practice: For enrichment, have students complete *Student Activity Book* page 70.

 Student Math Handbook: Students and families may use *Student Math Handbook* pages 144, 145, 155, 156 for reference and review. See pages 172–178 in the back of this unit.

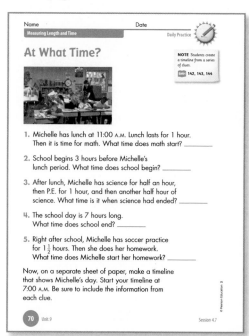

▲ Student Activity Book, p. 70

Professional Development

② **Teacher Note:** End-of-Unit Assessment, p. 160

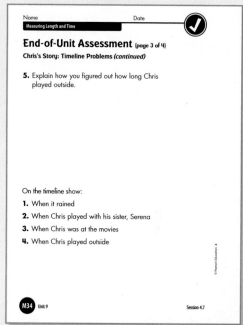

On the timeline show:
1. When it rained
2. When Chris played with his sister, Serena
3. When Chris was at the movies
4. When Chris played outside

▲ Resource Masters, M34

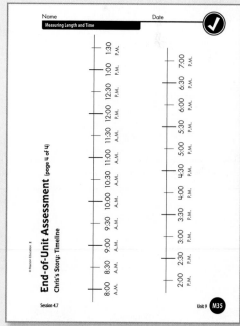

▲ Resource Masters, M35

Measuring Length and Time

In Part 6 of *Implementing Investigations in Grade 2,* you will find a set of Teacher Notes that addresses topics and issues applicable to the curriculum as a whole rather than to specific curriculum units. They include the following:

Computational Fluency and Place Value

Computational Algorithms and Methods

Representations and Contexts for Mathematical Work

Foundations of Algebra in the Elementary Grades

Discussing Mathematical Ideas

Racial and Linguistic Diversity in the Classroom:
   What Does Equity Mean in Today's Math Classroom?

Learning to Measure Length

Learning to measure and understanding what it means to measure involve more than learning how to use a ruler. These are challenging tasks that require repeated learning experiences over time.

Direct Comparison

When students compare lengths they often do so by placing them side by side. Direct comparison is only practical when measuring small or movable objects. Many students use direct comparison to measure with the strips in Investigation 1; they do so by placing an object against a strip to see if both have the same length. Students must decide which dimension of an object to compare to a strip. They may compare one dimension of an object to a strip— for example, the length of a book—but if the lengths do not match, they discard the object and go on to a different one. Because students may focus on one dimension and not consider different dimensions of an object, such as the book's width, they may not think about turning the object and comparing another of its dimensions as a possibility.

Indirect Comparison

When students are comparing two objects that can not be placed next to each other, they often introduce a third object such as a string or cube tower to compare lengths. For instance, students might indirectly compare an object to a strip by visually searching the room for an object that looks the same length as a given strip. Once an object is located, the student might cut a piece of string the same length as a specific dimension of the object, and then compare that string to the strip. A more efficient strategy would be to cut a piece of string the same length as the strip and then walk around the room comparing the string to various objects. If you see students using this strategy be sure to have them share it in a discussion.

Measuring with Units

Students use repeated units to measure the lengths of objects by counting how many unit lengths match the length of a dimension of the object. For instance, to find an object that is the length of one of the paper strips (Session 1.1), a student might find that one strip is three pencils long and then find an object in the classroom that is three pencils long.

As students are developing their understanding of linear measure, you will see variations in strategies and in accuracy. Some students can use this method only if they have enough unit lengths to place end to end for the entire length of the object. Other students use a single object and iterate it—that is, place it along the length of an object, mark its end, and then pick it up and place the length again, this time starting at its previous endpoint, and so on.

You may see students using various degrees of care in their unit iterations. Some may use their hands to iterate but pay little attention to whether there are any gaps or overlaps in their hands' placement. Some may think that several students' hands can be used, even though the hands are of different sizes. Such actions indicate that students, although beginning to understand the process of unit iteration, are unaware of a critical feature of measuring with units—that *a single unit* must be iterated, with no gaps or overlaps, to measure the length of an object.

As students work, ask questions to encourage them to reflect on the reliablility of their iteration strategies. The questions included here help students see that a unit must be used in a consistent way (for example, hands placed horizontally as opposed to horizontally *and* vertically) and carefully iterated. If not, they may get different measurements for the same object, even though they are measuring with the same unit. For instance, if students determine that a strip is 12 hands long when they measure the first time, but 8 hands when they measure it a second time, how can these numbers help them find an object the same length as the strip? How many hands long will the object have to be? 8? 12? 10? To help students think about this, ask questions such as the following:

Do you always get the same number when you measure the desk with your hands? Should you? Why?

Do you get the same number if you hold your hands this way [oriented vertically] and this way [oriented horizontally]? Why not?

What do you have to remember when you measure something with your hands?

The process of measuring length is more complex than it may initially seem. When students measure length, they are, in effect, separating a continuous distance into countable units. This is essentially the function of linear measurement tools, such as inch sticks, rulers, and yardsticks. However, students need many experiences using nonstandard materials to construct understanding of the process of measurement before they are able to meaningfully use measuring tools. They need opportunities to choose appropriate units for measuring length—for example, craft sticks, paper strips, and paper clips—and experiences lining up and counting units, or iterating a single unit, to measure length.

As students' understanding of measurement develops, they begin to formulate ideas about the need for a standard measuring tool, such as a ruler or yardstick. This is a time when using measuring tools becomes meaningful for students, and it is based on the conceptual understanding students develop through many experiences using nonstandard units to measure. The need for a standard measuring tool is developed throughout this unit. In Investigation 3, students use inches, feet, yards, centimeters, and meters to measure length.

Students use nonstandard materials to measure objects.

Teacher Note

Measuring and Comparing: How Far Can You Jump?

As students find and compare lengths, they draw on their knowledge of numbers. For instance, students use their understanding of number relationships when they measure an object using strips of one length, and then predict its measurement in strips of a related length, and when they discuss the various measurements that result when different units are used.

Students also apply their knowledge of number and comparing numbers as they solve problems about measurement. How Far Can You Jump? is an activity that lends itself to students' use of number relationships and strategies for comparing numbers. Some students may use counting on to find the difference between their longest and shortest jumps. In the student's work that follows, Anita shows how she used this strategy. Anita counted on from her shortest jump, 65, to her longest jump, 82, and found a difference of 17.

Other students, however, break apart and combine numbers, as Leo's work illustrates. Leo's longest jump was 112 and his shortest jump was 70. To find the difference, Leo added 30 to 70 to get to 100. Then, he added 12 to 30 to find a difference of 42.

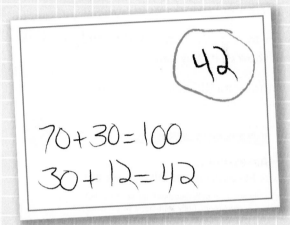

Leo's Work

Note that Leo thought of the problem as finding a missing part. Some students, as seen in Henry's work below, may see the problem as subtracting. Henry's longest jump was 83 and his shortest was 81. His equation shows the difference as part of the equation and not the solution.

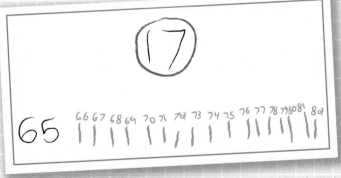

Anita's Work

$$83 - 2 = 81$$

Henry's Work

When students find the class's longest and shortest jumps (in Session 1.5), they will be able to compare their strategies for finding the difference between the same two numbers. Use this as an opportunity to discuss efficiency in solving mathematics problems. For example, Leo has solved the problems by "chunking" numbers, a more efficient strategy than counting by ones.

Assessment: A Measurement Disagreement

Benchmarks addressed:

Benchmark 1: Identify sources of measurement error.

Benchmark 3: Recognize that, when measuring the same length, larger units yield smaller counts. (By the end of the unit, the benchmark more specifically states that students should recognize that, when measuring the same length, larger units yield smaller counts.)

In order to meet the benchmarks, students' work should show that they can:

- List reasons for differences in measurements.

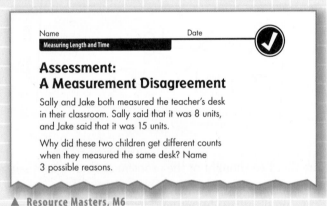

Name   Date

Measuring Length and Time   ✓

Assessment:
A Measurement Disagreement

Sally and Jake both measured the teacher's desk in their classroom. Sally said that it was 8 units, and Jake said that it was 15 units.

Why did these two children get different counts when they measured the same desk? Name 3 possible reasons.

▲ **Resource Masters, M6**

Meeting the Benchmarks

Students who meet the benchmark identify three different reasons why Sally and Jake would get different counts. Three basic themes that arise in these students' responses are that Sally and Jake used different units to measure, that one or both measured inaccurately (students might suggest different reasons for the error), and that they measured different dimensions of the desk.

Amaya listed the following to explain why Sally and Jake get different counts.

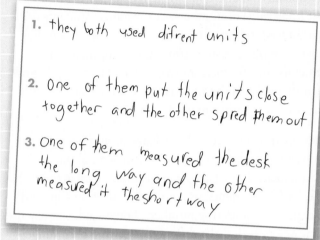

1. they both used difrent units

2. One of them put the units close together and the other spred them out

3. one of them measured the desk the long way and the other measured it the short way

Amaya's Work

Malcolm addressed the same three themes in his work.

1. They used different items.
2. They miscounted.
3. They might have measured different parts.

1. thay useted pirrint itums

2. thay MSConted

3. they Mite or mesher pifrint parts

Malcolm's Work

Nadia did not suggest that the students might have measured different dimensions of the desk, but did identify three possible sources of error.

> 1. They used different things to mesure with.
>
> 2. They left spaces bettween were they put it down like ths much [≡]
>
> 3. They overlapped each other

Nadia's Work

When the teacher saw Simon's work, she asked him to read his responses aloud to her so that she could interpret his thinking.

1. One of the other units is really bigger than the other units.
2. They could have measured different parts of the tables.
3. They could have guessed a random number.

> 1. 1 ov the oth cwings is really Bigr than the thet Cuhc
>
> 2. thet cod ov mosrd dirrit Prsuv the togl.
>
> 3. thet cod ov gast a rouhdm nomBr

Simon's Work

The teacher asked Simon to explain his third reason. He suggested that maybe they counted the units and then went to write the number on their paper but forgot the actual number, so they wrote a "random" number rather than recounting the units.

Partially Meeting the Benchmarks

Students who partially meet the benchmarks identify one or two different reasons that Sally and Jake got different counts.

Holly's first two responses are essentially the same reason.

Note that Holly suggests that Jake's unit might be bigger than Sally's. In fact, since Sally got the smaller count, if they both correctly measured the same length, her unit must be *bigger*. At this point in the unit, students are not expected to recognize this inverse relationship. They will work on this idea in Investigations 2 and 3.

Ask students who partially meet the benchmarks whether Sally or Jake might have made an error and, if so, what might have caused that error.

> 1. they mesured with difrent matirialls.
>
> 2. Jakes unit is bigger than sallys
>
> 3. They mesured difrennt wase one mesured accros and one mesured down

Holly's Work

Not Meeting the Benchmarks

Darren offered three reasons, but only the first reflects an understanding of the measurement process.

Ask students who do not meet the benchmarks if there is any way that both Jake and Sally could be correct.

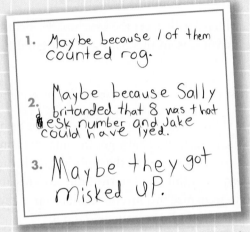

1. Maybe because 1 of them counted rog.

2. Maybe because Sally britanded that 8 was that esk number and Jake could have lyed.

3. Maybe they got misked up.

Darren's Work

Cubes, Tiles, and Inch-Bricks

On *Student Activity Book* pages 21–22 and 23–24, students measure a variety of lengths shorter than 12 inches. Some problems identify the length in terms of an object to measure (e.g., the length of Princess Funer's cloak is the same as the length of your pencil) and others identify the length in terms of a number of units (e.g., the length of Ren's jacket is the same as the length of 9 cubes). Since students have previously measured lengths in terms of cubes and tiles, they may be confused about why they need to measure the length in terms of inch-bricks. After all, why should they measure Ren's jacket if they already know it's 9 cubes long?

If this happens, remind students of the story, "Measuring in the Land of Inch," and point out that the people in the Land of Inch must now measure everything in inch-bricks. They do this so they can make comparisons when they need to. For example, if Ren needs to replace his jacket, he will need to give the tailor his measurements in terms of Inch-Bricks. Because the King has declared that everyone should measure with Inch-Bricks, the tailor has inch-bricks to help him measure, but he might not have cubes.

Some problems identify the length to be measured in terms of a number of tiles. Even if students have referred to these as "inch-tiles," they may not have made a connection between the length of each side of a tile and the length of an inch-brick. Having students lay out the length in terms of tiles and then measure with inch-bricks helps them develop the idea of an inch as a unit of length rather than as a physical object (a tile or rectangular piece of card stock).

For example, consider Henry who is measuring the length of Nim's pants, which is the same length as 4 tiles.

Henry: Hey, that's funny. I got 4 inch-bricks and it was 4 tiles. Maybe the tiles are as long as the bricks. (Henry uses his measuring tool to measure the length of one tile.)

Teacher: So how long is one tile?

Henry: One inch.

When Henry gets to the problem to find the length of Princess Funer's castle (on *Student Activity Book* page 23), which is about as long as the table, Henry decides to measure the table with tiles because they're the same as the inch-bricks. Even though the lesson is designed to have students measure objects using their measuring tools, the teacher allows Henry to measure the table with tiles. After he finishes, the teacher asks him to measure the table again, this time using the inch-brick measuring tool, to make sure that he gets the same number of inches. This gives him greater confidence that using either the inch-brick measuring tool or the tiles provides the same result.

Assessment: The King's Foot

Students read the story, "The King's Foot" and then write and draw a picture to show why the stall for the princess's horse was too small.

Benchmark addressed:

Benchmark 2: Recognize that the same count of different-sized units yields different lengths.

In order to meet the benchmark, students' work should show that they can:

- Explain differences in measurement.

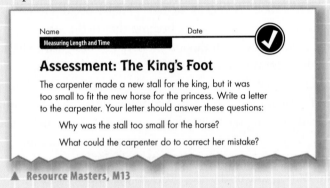

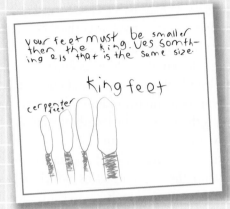
Carla's Work

▲ **Resource Masters, M13**

Meeting the Benchmark

Students who meet the benchmark explain that the reason the stall ended up too small is that the carpenter's foot is smaller than the king's foot.

Carla explained to the carpenter, "Your feet must be smaller than the king's. Use something else that is the same size."

Luis wrote the following:

"Dear carpenter, The stall was too small for the horse because the king's feet must be bigger than a foot. To fix your mistake, you need to measure the king's foot. Then do it all over again."

Luis' Work

Carla and Luis resolve the problem by suggesting that the carpenter use a unit that is the same length as the king's foot. Their solution rests on the idea that the carpenter and the king need to rely on a common unit.

Roshaun realizes that the cause of the error is that the king and the carpenter used different-sized units, but comes up with a different way to correct the mistake. "Dear Carpenter,

The reason why the stable is smaller is because you didn't use the same size feet as the king. To fix it, first you have to wreck it. Then you can put the horse in the spot and build the stable around it. After that, you take the horse out and you have a perfect stable for the princess's horse."

Roshaun's Work

The teacher can ask Roshaun if there is another way to rebuild the stable and be sure that it is the correct size, even if the carpenter can't bring the horse to stand in the spot.

Partially Meeting the Benchmark

The writing of students who partially meet the benchmark indicates some thinking about units, but these students have not clearly stated what the issue is. Monisha wrote, "The stall was too small because the horse was bigger than the stall. To correct the stall, you could use a ruler."

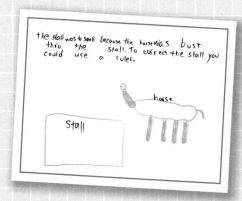

Monisha's Work

Monisha should be asked to explain why the error occurred in the first place and how the ruler could be used to correct it.

Not Meeting the Benchmark

Some students offer measurement-related reasons for the error that are not about the different sized units. For example, Juan wrote,

"Dear Carpenter, The barn is too small and I think maybe you counted wrong. Or maybe you should make another barn and make sure that you try your best and try to make sure that you won't be wrong."

Juan's Work

The teacher should ask Juan if it is possible that the carpenter actually counted correctly and measured with her footlengths correctly, but still ended up with a barn that is too small.

Benchmarks on the Body

Carpenters used to make marks on their workbenches to indicate lengths that they often used, such as 2 inches, 4 inches, or 1 foot. These *benchmarks* speeded up the measuring process, since the carpenter did not then need to find a measuring tape or ruler every time. In a similar way, identifying benchmarks on the body is useful because we often need to estimate measurements when we don't have a ruler handy. They provide a way for us to visualize standard measures.

You can help your students find such benchmarks. For instance, an inch is about the size of the first joint on the thumb. Ask students to check this out with their rulers or inch sticks to see if it's true for them. They can then use their rulers or inch-brick tools to find a place on the body that is 1 foot long. One possibility is the forearm. Or, they may find something that they can double: if a hand span measures 6 inches, 2 of these equal 1 foot.

Teachers who have had students find benchmarks on their bodies, and then have shown them how to use those benchmarks to estimate other lengths have found that it helps their students internalize the measures. They are able to estimate measurements with reference to their own bodies and no longer feel the need to rely on a ruler all the time. One third grade teacher overheard his students giving each other directions to pour water into a glass. The first student asked, "How full?" and the second responded, while looking at her thumb, "About 2 inches."

Once benchmarks on the body are established, it is important to use these measurements as much as possible every day in school. Teachers have found ways to weave measurement into lining up for recess ("Everyone whose little finger is less than 3 inches can line up now") or doing tasks at the end of the school day ("Find an object that's between 5 and 6 inches long and put it away"). If you have your students first estimate with their benchmarks and later use a ruler to check their estimates, you will be helping them internalize a system of measurement. That skill will help them tremendously, both in mathematics classes and in their daily lives.

Learning to Use a Ruler

In creating their own measuring tools, students come to see that these tools number and iterate units of measure, facilitating the process of measuring. Comparing their own measuring tools to rulers helps them to identify these features of conventional tools.

As students use conventional rulers, they have more to learn about the use of measuring tools. This Teacher Note describes some of the common difficulties that arise.

A common error is to confuse units (linear distances) with locations on the tool. For example, when asked to show an inch, a child might point to the number 1, or to a single point. This child must come to see that an inch is indicated by the interval, a distance, between two lines, or two numbers.

A related confusion is why the 1 appears some distance into the ruler, rather than at the end. Once students realize that the 1 represents the 1-inch distance from the end of the ruler, they come to think of the end of the ruler as 0.

Some students, when using a ruler, focus only on one endpoint of the object being measured, rather than the distance between the beginning and ending points. These students might identify the length of the line below as 5 inches, because it ends at 5, rather than 4 inches, the distance between the points marked 1 and 5.

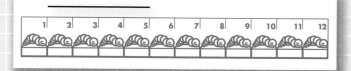

Similarly, some students may be unaware that any point on the ruler can be used as a starting point. That is, the placement of the ruler gives the correct measurement of 4 inches, just as it would if the 0-end of the ruler were placed at the beginning of the line.

Students must also attend to the orientation of their ruler—which end of the ruler they use as their starting point. If students placed the 12-inch end of the ruler at the beginning of the 4-inch line, then simply read off the number on the ruler that matched the end of the line, they would say the line is 8 inches long.

If students do this, ask them to look at the length of what they are measuring and to think about their inch-bricks or other benchmarks. Ask, "Does the line look like it is 8 inches long?"

Background on the Metric System

Only a few countries in the world currently use nonmetric measures of length. Most countries agreed, at various points in the last century, to use the metric system. Scientists worldwide use the metric system so that they can easily compare results and have a common measurement language. Thus scientists in the United States are quite familiar with the metric system, but most other citizens are not.

Besides the United States, Liberia also makes use of the nonmetric system. Freed slaves from the United States were instrumental in founding the country of Liberia in the early 1800s. One of the customs they brought into their new country was the U.S. Standard system of measurement (sometimes called customary or English measure). It has remained the commonly used system of measurement to this day. Myanmar (Burma) is the only other country not using metric measurement.

The United States has resisted attempts to convert to metric. Americans have repeatedly resisted these efforts in part because the U.S. Standard system is familiar and it is difficult to learn to use a new system. As early as the 1800s, legislation was introduced to use the metric system. In the 1980s, there was another major effort to introduce the metric system into our lives. Remember when speed limit signs were posted in both kilometers and miles per hour? This new attempt, sponsored by a special Metric Office in the U.S. government, largely failed. Because our country is large and somewhat isolated from countries in which the metric system is commonly used, we remain stuck in our ways.

U.S. adherence to the nonmetric system has caused some problems, both frustrating and amusing. For example, athletes in this country frequently use U.S. Standard measurements in their local, regional, and national competitions. U.S. swimmers typically compete in races that involve multiples of 25 yards, and most pools in this country are 25 yards long, start to finish. But when these swimmers compete in international races, the distances are all multiples of 25 meters. To prepare for international competition, coaches sometimes have their swimmers practice metric races, which of course end somewhere in the middle of the pool!

Teacher Note

Working With Timelines

As a part of the final unit in Grade 2, students work on representing time. This *Investigation* is placed at the end of the school year because it builds on experience from previous Grade 2 work, including the *What Time Is It?* routine and the fractions unit, *Parts of a Whole, Parts of a Group*. Students in Grade 2 require the opportunity for extended work with the many mathematical concepts that support the telling of time.

These sessions provide grounded work about time, serving many mathematical and practical purposes. There are three main activities woven throughout the six sessions: School Day Timeline, Fred & Winnipeg Timelines, and Special Day Timelines. Each of these activities provides opportunities for students to hear the variety of phrases commonly used for different times, such as *quarter past* and *quarter 'til*, and for intervals of time, such as *half-hour, half an hour, one half hour,* and *half of an hour*. This work also provides the practical opportunity to connect times of day with typical events from their lives and to see how two 12-hour periods make up the 24-hour day.

This Investigation also provides students with an opportunity to apply concepts they have learned over the course of the school year. An analog clock uses two, and sometimes three, different units: hours, minutes, and sometimes seconds. The features of the clock take on different meanings for each unit of measure. For example, the 12 numerals on the clock may represent the hours of a 12-hour period or some number of groups of 5 minutes within an hour. Understanding time requires the ability to coordinate these two units. In the first three investigations of measurement, students learned that if two people measure something using different-sized units, they get a different total count for each. This idea applies to measuring time in hours and minutes. For example, the amount of time from 2:00 to 3:30 can be represented as $1\frac{1}{2}$ hours, 90 minutes, or 1 hour and 30 minutes.

Throughout the curriculum, there is emphasis on representing an idea in a variety of ways. Before students begin this Investigation, they are already familiar with two conventional representations of time: analog and digital clocks. This new representation highlights features of time that can remain hidden in the analog and digital representations. A timeline represents time by using length. An amount of time is proportional to the part of the line that represents it: a part of the line that represents 2 hours is twice as long as a part that represents 1 hour and 4 times as long as a part that represents a half hour.

A timeline allows students to focus on duration. Students can easily see which events last for longer or shorter periods of time based on the total lengths of these events as represented on the timeline. They can also see how the timeline can be extended forward and backward. As they imagine extending it, students can visualize how the 24-hour cycle repeats over and over again.

A timeline also uses ideas introduced in the Grade 2 unit, *Parts of a Whole, Parts of a Group: Fractions*. An hour can be divided into 2 equal half hours, or 4 equal quarter-hours. Students have worked with these ideas in the *What Time Is It?* routine throughout Grade 2. Because students have already worked with wholes, halves and quarters before, they apply this understanding when calculating duration on the timeline in hours, half-hours, and/or quarter-hours.

Students will continue to build on the ideas from this Investigation in Grades 3 and 4. The representation of time on a horizontal axis lays the foundation for graphs involving change over time. On such graphs, values on the *x*-axis represent some unit of time and changes in the values on the *y*-axis (such as, for example, temperature) can be seen as one looks from left to right along the graph.

End-of-Unit Assessment

Problem 1: Inches and Centimeters

Benchmarks addressed:

Benchmark 3: Recognize that, when measuring the same length, larger units yield smaller counts.

Benchmark 4: Measure objects using inches and centimeters.

Benchmark 5: Use a ruler to measure lengths longer than one foot.

In order to meet the benchmarks, students' work should show that they can:

- Explain why the measure of a length is fewer inches than centimeters;

- Find the length of a line in inches and centimeters;

- Find the length of a 17-inch piece of adding machine tape using a ruler.

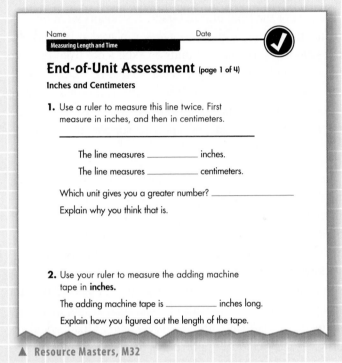

▲ Resource Masters, M32

Meeting Benchmark 3

Students who meet the benchmark indicate that smaller units measure a shorter length and yield a higher count or that larger units measure a greater length and yield a lower count. For example, Alberto writes, "The inches are bigger and it takes up more space with one inch than with one centimeter."

> the inches are biger and it takes up more space with one inch than whith one centimeater.

Alberto's Work

Juanita identified centimeter ("cm") as the unit that gives a greater number, "Because the cm is smaller, you can fit more."

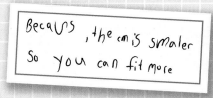

Juanita's Work

Partially Meeting Benchmark 3

Students who partially meet the benchmark offer a true response that is related to the question, but do not mention the size of the unit. For example, Gregory correctly identifies centimeter as the unit that gives a greater number and writes, "Centimeters give more numbers."

Gregory's Work

If students offer a response like this, ask, "Why do centimeters give a larger number?"

Not Meeting Benchmark 3

Students who do not meet the benchmark offer a reason that is not related to measurement. For example, Jeffery, who measured the line as 12 centimeters, writes that 12 gives you a greater number, "because it's an even number and that it's more higher than 5."

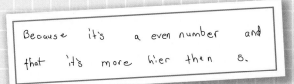

Jeffery's Work

Meeting Benchmark 4

Students who meet the benchmark correctly measure the line to be about 5 inches and about 13 centimeters. Since the line is actually a little more than 5 inches, some students might say $5\frac{1}{2}$ inches or $5\frac{1}{4}$ inches.

Not Meeting Benchmark 4

Students who find a length of 6 inches and 14 centimeters do not meet the benchmark. These students are probably not placing the end of the ruler at the end of the line, but instead are lining up the number 1 with the end of the line. Talk to these students about their measurement technique. They may not understand that the ruler marks off units of length, and the first unit extends from the end of the ruler to where the 1 appears.

They may benefit from opportunities to measure objects using both the ruler and the inch-bricks. Students will continue to work with linear measurement in Grade 3.

Meeting Benchmark 5

Students who meet the benchmark accurately measure the adding machine tape as 17 inches and can explain their strategy for measuring a length longer than 12 inches. For example, Alberto writes, "I measured it. It was one foot, so I put my finger where the foot ended. Then I measured the rest."

Alberto's Work

Juanita writes, "I put the ruler on the tape. Then I noticed that it was not enough so I drew a dot to show that is where to start."

> I Put the ruler on the tape then
> I Notist that it was not enifso i Drue
> a Dot to show thats wore to sart

Juanita's Work

Jeffery writes, "The ruler is not long enough, so I put my finger there and slid the ruler up."

> the ruler is not long enouf.
> So I put my finger there
> and slid the ruler up.

Jeffery's Work

Partially Meeting Benchmark 5

Students who partially meet the benchmark can accurately measure a length longer than 12 inches, but are unable to explain their strategy in writing. For example, Anita writes, "I used the ruler to figure out how many inches long it was."

> I used the ruler to figur out
> how meany inches long it whas

Anita's Work

While it is true that everybody used a ruler to measure the tape, Anita has not explained what she must do to measure a length longer than a ruler. Ask such students to show you how they measured and have them tell you what they are doing as they are doing it.

Not Meeting Benchmark 5

Students who do not meet the benchmark do not have a strategy for measuring a length longer than 12 inches.

Problem 2: Chris's Story

Benchmarks addressed:

Benchmark 6: Solve problems involving the beginning time of an event, ending time of an event, and duration of the event; given two of these, find the third for events beginning and ending on the hour or half hour.

Benchmark 7: Use a timeline to record and determine duration to the hour or half hour

In order to meet the benchmarks, students' work should show that they can:

• Correctly determine durations and times in the problems;

• Represent the events correctly on the timeline.

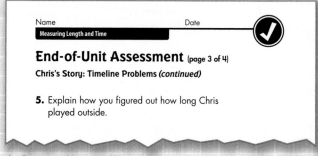

Name _____ Date _____

Measuring Length and Time

End-of-Unit Assessment (page 3 of 4)

Chris's Story: Timeline Problems *(continued)*

5. Explain how you figured out how long Chris played outside.

▲ Resource Masters, M34

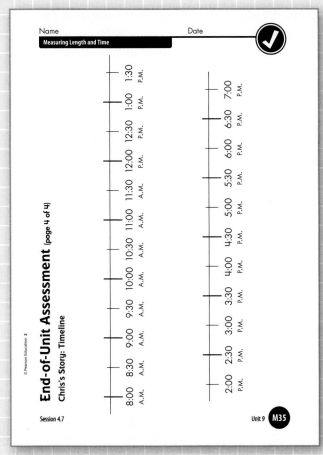

▲ Resource Masters, M35

Meeting the Benchmarks

Students who meet the benchmark correctly use the information in Chris's Story to determine the duration of the events. The corresponding duration and times of these events are then shown on the timeline.

For example, in Questions 4 and 5 students determine how long Chris played outside when he played from 4:00 P.M. to 6:30 P.M. Students first calculate the duration in Question 4 and explain how they calculated it in Question 5. Then they write this event on the timeline. Lonzell explained how he calculated the duration.

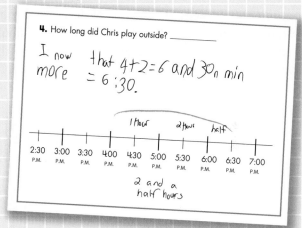

Lonzell's Work

5. Explain how you figured out how long Chris played outside.

I used the time line and I Jumped 1 hour and then I Jumped anothes and then I Jumped a half an hour and I got 2 hours and a half.

Lonzell's Work

Partially Meeting the Benchmarks

Some students may miscalculate the duration for one of the Questions 1–4, but then accurately draw the event on the timeline, or vice versa. For example, Carolina calculated the duration for Question 4 as 2 hours from 4:00 P.M. to 6:30 P.M. However, the way that she drew the event on the timeline reflects the accurate duration of the event. Ask a student like Carolina to explain how she arrived at 2 hours to determine whether or not she can correctly interpret the interval drawn on the timeline.

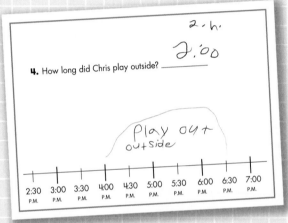

Carolina's Work

Other students may calculate the duration correctly, but do not provide an explanation that reflects that understanding. For example, Henry correctly calculated the same event's duration as "2 and a half hours." He explains this by writing, "I counted in my head." Again, you can ask this student to further explain what he counted.

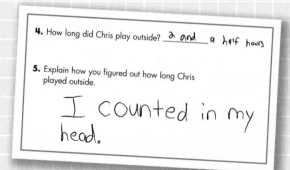

Henry's Work

For students who partially meet the benchmark, encourage them to use the timeline to determine the duration and check their answers. Talk to these students about counting the number of hours and half hours of the events on the timeline.

Not Meeting the Benchmarks

Students who do not meet the benchmark provide durations that are not consistent with the information in the story. For example, Katrina writes the events on her timeline at times and for durations that do not reflect the information given in the story.

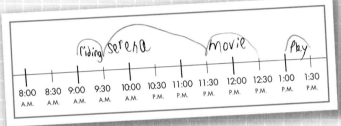

Katrina's Work

Understanding duration and elapsed time is a challenging idea for many second graders. As their sense of time matures and as they become more confident in telling time and understanding the structure of the analog clock, they gradually develop a clear understanding of these complex ideas of measuring time. In Grade 3, students will continue to build on the work in this unit through telling time, working with 5-minute intervals, and representing time on a horizontal axis.

Matching Lengths

In a discussion following the activity Scavenger Hunt 1 (page 27), these students are sharing their strategies for comparing lengths. They describe and demonstrate the ways they used direct comparison, indirect comparison, and nonstandard units to match objects to the length of the paper strips.

Teacher: Let's share some of the ways you are finding things in the classroom that are as long as our paper strips. What did you use to help you compare lengths?

Alberto: We used cubes. The first strip is as long as 27 cubes.

Teacher: Did anyone else use cubes? How did the cubes work? Nadia?

Nadia: The cubes worked OK, but sometimes they weren't exactly the right length, but between. That made it harder. And sometimes, if you had to use a lot of cubes, it was hard. The cubes broke apart.

Teacher: It sounds like when you used cubes you could tell if something was about the same length as a paper strip. *About* the same length is fine. It doesn't have to be exact.

Teacher: Nadia's experience with the cubes makes me think that cubes might be hard to use when the paper strip is long, like Strip [B]. What other measuring tool could you use to help you compare a long paper strip to an object?

Rochelle: We used string.

Teacher: How did that work? Did you put the string next to the strip?

Rochelle: On top of it. And then Tia cut it. And then we compared it to things, and we found out that the blue table is the same length as Strip [B].

Teacher: Did anyone else use other ways? Juan?

Juan: For the shortest Strip, [D], I used my knuckle. It was 16 knuckles long. Then for the strip in the middle, I measured with my hands and I got 8.

Teacher: Can you show us how you measured Strip [C] with your hands, Juan?

Juan demonstrates alternately placing his left and right hands, heel to fingertip, along the paper strip, counting as he does so: 1, 2, 3, 4, 5, 6, 7, 8.

Teacher: Juan used two different ways to compare strips. Did other people use more than one way? (Several hands go up.) Carla?

Carla: Well, Strip [D] is pretty short, so we just held things up next to it. And Strip [B] is very long, so we held string up to it and cut it the same length. Then we compared that to things in the room.

Dialogue Box

Using Related Units of Measure

In Scavenger Hunt 2: Blue and Yellow Strips, students find objects in the classroom that are a certain number of nonstandard units long. They then predict and determine the length of the objects when they are measured with a second related nonstandard unit. The lengths of the units the students use, blue strips and yellow strips, are in a 2-to-1 relationship.

During Math Workshop, two students are searching for something that is 5 blue strips long. The teacher notices Simon lay 5 strips along the edge of a bookshelf with gaps between the strips.

Teacher: What have you found?

Simon: This bookshelf is 5 blue strips long.

Teacher: Does it matter that there is space between the end of the strips?

Henry: Yeah, you've got to push them together, Simon.

Simon: But then they won't fit. The shelf is longer.

The teacher measures the length of a nearby table, by laying 5 more blue strips end-to-end.

Teacher: Are the bookshelf and this table the same length? Are they both 5 strips long?

Simon: No, the bookshelf is longer than the table. The table is 5 strips long.

Simon writes *table* on his student sheet and looks at the next question, "What is 4 blue strips long?" He lays 4 strips end to end on the table, looks around the room, and then decides it would be easier to measure with a piece of string. He cuts a string the length of the 4 blue strips, then walks around the room looking for something to match its length.

In a later session, the teacher discusses the activity with the class. Now the conversation focuses on the 2-to-1 relationship.

Teacher: If you had already measured something with blue strips, how did you figure out how many yellow strips it was going to be?

Juanita: I thought of how you go 2, 4, 6, 8, 10, and I went like that because 2 yellows would fill in 1 blue.

Teacher: Juanita counted the blue strips by 2s. Did anyone use a different method?

Jacy: I doubled the number of blue strips.

Teacher: Why?

Jacy: Because 2 yellow strips makes 1 blue strip. It takes 2 yellow for every blue strip.

Teacher: So Jacy doubled the number of blue strips. When I put a blue strip next to a yellow strip, like this (places strips side by side), you can see that the blue strip is twice as long as the yellow strip.

Teacher: Remember what we measured with 3 blue strips?

Nate: My desk.

Teacher: Which way?

Nate: This way [gestures to indicate width].

Teacher: Right, the width. So how many yellow?

Nate: 6.

Because of the previous work in Grade 2 with doubling numbers, students are often quite facile with determining the length of an object using blue and yellow strips.

Dialogue Box

What's the Length and What's the Width?

The following discussion took place in Session 3.2 as the teacher was introducing Measure and Compare (page 89). The same issues are likely to arise in Investigation 1 as students measure objects in the classroom.

Teacher: One of the comparisons that you'll be doing is comparing the *width* of a dictionary to the *length* of your reading book. I have the dictionary right here. What part should you measure if you want to find the *width*?

Chen: I think you should measure the part that goes along the bottom.

Tia: Yeah, because width is how wide something is. It's almost the same word, *width* and *wide*. So I think the bottom edge, too.

Holly: I think you should measure this part—the fattest part. (Holly points to the binding of the book.)

Teacher: So, Holly, you're suggesting we measure the distance between the front and back cover?

Holly: Right!

Monisha: I don't think that's the width, even though that part is kind of wide. I think that part is called the *thickness* of the dictionary.

Leo: Well, I think that width is the widest part of something, so I think you should measure from top to bottom.

Jeffrey: I disagree with Leo because I think that if you measure from the top to the bottom, that's like measuring how tall it is, and I think you'd be measuring the *length* of the dictionary, not the *width*. I think the width goes from left to right, and the length goes from top to bottom.

Leigh: But what happens to the length and the width when you turn the dictionary the other way so that it's on its side? Then does the length become the width and the width become the length? This is getting confusing.

Teacher: You're right! I'm feeling a little confused about the length and width, too.

Melissa Hey, I know. Why don't we look it up in the dictionary that you are holding! (Looks up the definition of *width* and reads it aloud.) *Width*—the quality or condition of being wide; the size of something in terms of how wide it is.

Jeffrey: That doesn't help at all. We already knew that.

The confusion over the definitions of *length* and *width* is not uncommon. These terms are somewhat dependent on the context and situation. The most frequently used definitions are 1) *length* is the distance from top to bottom and *width* is the distance from side to side or 2) *length* is the longer dimension and *width* is the shorter dimension. When measuring 3D objects, like the dictionary, the measurement from front to back is often referred to as the *depth* of the object. An additional complication is that the term *length* is also the general term to indicate the measure of *any* line segment from end to end.

What is most important in measuring objects is that everyone agrees on how to define the *length* and *width* so that the terms are used consistently among the group.

The Need for Measuring Tools

Working on *Student Activity Book* page 19, students have measured various lengths, using loose inch-bricks (1″ × $\frac{1}{2}$″ rectangles cut from card stock). Then, in order to motivate the use of the inch-brick measuring tool, the teacher brings them together to discuss the difficulties they had.

Teacher: What were some problems you found while you were measuring? Why did students get different measurements?

Henry: They always moved. When you tried to find how long the paper was, they got messed up.

Teacher: So while you were measuring, it was hard to keep the inch-bricks straight. Was that frustrating?

Class: Yes.

Teacher: Can that affect your measurements?

Class: Yes.

Teacher: What other things could affect your measurements?

Alberto: They could have measured different measurements like they could have gone one way and another kid could have measured it the other way.

Teacher: For example, what would the length of the glue stick be? Here (points up and down) or here (points across the width)?

Paige: Up and down would be the length.

Teacher: Is this what you mean, Alberto?

Alberto: Oh, I'm thinking if you put the bricks together a different way.

Teacher: Oh, so if you put the bricks this way rather than this way.

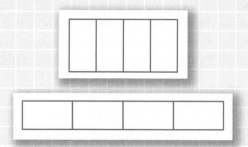

Juan: That could have happened and you would have gotten a much bigger answer.

Teacher: OK, should we measure end to end or side to side?

Class: End to end.

Juan: Or they might have been spaced apart or they overlapped.

Teacher: The people in the Land of Inch all had these very same problems. So Princess Funer came up with another idea.

The teacher reads the next installment of the story "Measuring in the Land of Inch" to explain the inch-brick measuring tool. This tool stabilizes the units so that students can measure lengths more accurately. It provides a transition to the ruler, which students will use in the next Investigation. At this point, using the tool with inch-bricks pasted down helps students understand the connection between the discrete units they have been counting and units as they appear on a ruler.

Dialogue Box

Measuring Lengths Longer Than 24 Inches

Throughout the unit, students work on the idea that a unit can be iterated. For example, to measure a table that is 6 measuring tools long, students do not need to lay out 6 tools. Instead, they can repeatedly place down a single tool, each time marking off where the tool ends and then placing the beginning of the tool at that spot.

Tia, a student who has been struggling all year with breaking numbers apart into 10s and 1s and with seeing 10 simultaneously as ten 1s and one 10, has iterated her inch-brick measuring tool to find that the table is 6 tools long. However, she's not sure what to do with that information.

Teacher: How many inch-bricks are in 2 tools?

Tia: I don't know.

Teacher: How many in 1 tool?

Tia: 12.

The teacher places the tool at the end of the table to measure the first 12 inches. Then she places the tool to show the second foot.

Teacher: OK. So let's move this tool to here. Now this length is 2 measuring tools long. So how many inches are in 2 measuring tools?

Tia points to the first brick on the tool and says, "13." Then she continues to count, 14, 15, . . . , 24, pointing to one brick for each number.

Teacher: OK. So there are 24 inch-bricks in 2 tools. How many in 3?

At first Tia is unsure what to do.

Teacher: Now do the same thing you did for 2 tools.

Tia points to the first brick on the measuring tool, says "25," and continues to point and count to 36. She now applies this method of counting bricks to determine the number of inch-bricks in 4, 5, and 6 measuring tools.

The teacher helps her keep track by holding up a finger for each measuring tool she has counted. She knows to stop when the teacher has 6 fingers up.

As they measure lengths longer than 24 inches, students work with several mathematical ideas. First, students work on the idea of iterating units. They come to see that, even though they may have numbered the bricks 1, 2, 3, . . . , as they reapply the tool, those inch-bricks might represent the 13th, 14th, and 15th inches in the length being measured, or the 25th, 26th, and 27th inches, or the 37th, 38th, and 39th inches, and so forth.

The task of measuring lengths longer than 24 inches also gives students practice with adding 2-digit numbers. Although Tia counted, most second graders will apply their knowledge of addition and of place value. For example, Juanita said, "It's six 10s, that's 60. Then you add on the twos—62, 64, 66, 68, 70, 72."

Whether they count or add, in this problem (of finding the number of inch-bricks in a length of 6 measuring tools), students are also working on the idea of multiplication. They are working with equal groups. As Tia measures the table in inch-bricks, she needs to keep track of two counts, inch-bricks and measuring tools, at the same time. While Tia counts inch-bricks, the teacher helps her keep track of the number of groups of 12 by holding up a finger for each tool that has been counted. This activity provides a new context in which she can work on how a number can represent both a group and a collection of 1s.

Dialogue Box

Not Even a Second Has Gone By: Calculating Duration

In this conversation, students are talking about Fred & Winnipeg: Chapter 1. As they work on calculating duration, students talk about what it is that they are counting. Instead of counting the intervals of time, some students count the discreet numbers, or digital labels.

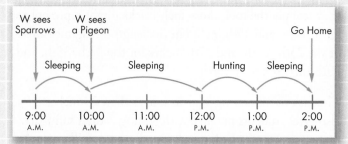

Teacher: How long is it from the time Winnipeg sees sparrows until the time she sees a pigeon?

Rochelle: One hour. I know because from nine o'clock to ten o'clock is one hour.

Teacher: How long is it from the time Winnipeg saw the pigeon until the time they stopped hunting?

Unlike the first question, this one requires that students consider more than one event over a period of hours.

Esteban: Three hours.

Travis: No, it's four hours.

Teacher: Why do you say four hours?

Travis: Because she sees a pigeon where it says 10. And then I counted from there. 10, 11, 12, 1. That's 4 hours.

Juanita: I disagree. I think it's three hours. Because you start at 10. And from 10 to 12 is 2 hours, and it's 1 hour more, so that's 3 hours altogether.

Teacher: Esteban, is that what you were thinking?

Esteban: I thought three, too. But I got it because I counted 10, 11, 12, and 1. That's four. And I know that you need to minus one from the numbers you count, so that's three. So it's three hours.

Esteban has developed a strategy for calculating duration on the timeline, although from his explanation it is not clear whether he understands the concept of duration or if he noticed a pattern. Since there are four labels from 10 to 1, he counts those and has realized that the number of hours will be 1 less than this amount. While he has reached the correct answer of three hours, his explanation does not reflect knowledge about how much time has passed.

Paige: I'm not sure what he means.

Teacher: Can you tell me where those three hours are on the timeline, Esteban? Who can tell me where the three hours are?

Katrina: They start at the 10 and end at the 1. So there are two hours from 10 to 12, and then one more hour from 12 to 1.

Teacher: Why do you think some people thought it was four hours?

Esteban: I think maybe because there are 4 numbers. Like, it starts at 10 and goes 10, 11, 12, 1.

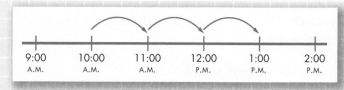

Rochelle: Yeah, but at 10, it's like nothing has happened. Not even a second has gone by yet. So when you get to 11, that's when it's one hour. Because from 10 to 11 o'clock is like one hour going by, and then 11 to 12 o'clock is like another hour going by. That's two hours, and then from 12 to 1 is another hour. So it's three hours altogether.

When thinking about calculating duration, students may develop strategies, like Esteban did, that do not reflect the concept of passing time. Esteban's explanation of counting the labels to determine duration is an incorrect strategy that students sometimes employ not just when calculating duration, but also in other work on number lines and in addition and subtraction. In such instances, bring students back to the timeline and ask them to show where they see hours on the timeline, reminding them to first locate the beginning time and then indicating what one hour would look like by *jumping,* or moving one step, to the next hour. Students who continue to struggle should have repeated experiences working with timelines marked in one-hour intervals, before going on to work with half- or quarter-hour intervals.

Student Math Handbook

The *Student Math Handbook* pages related to this unit are pictured on the following pages. This book is designed to be used flexibly: as a resource for students doing classwork, as a book students can take home for reference while doing homework and playing math games with their families, and as a reference for families to better understand the work their children are doing in class.

When students take the *Student Math Handbook* home, they and their families can discuss these pages together to reinforce or enhance students' understanding of the mathematical concepts and games in this unit.

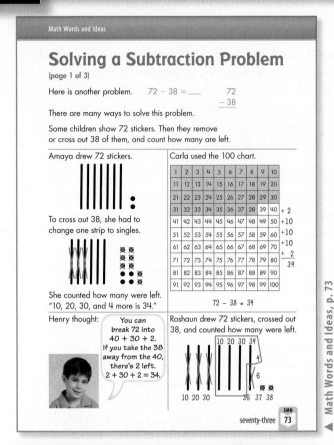

◀ Math Words and Ideas, p. 73

◀ Math Words and Ideas, p. 74

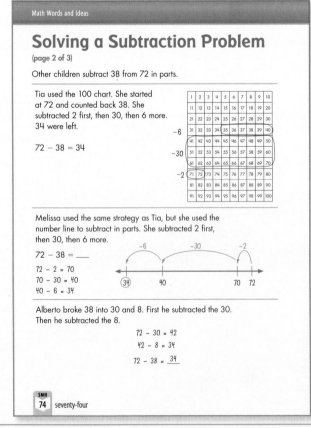

◀ Math Words and Ideas, p. 75

Tools for Measuring Time

Here are some tools for measuring and keeping track of time:

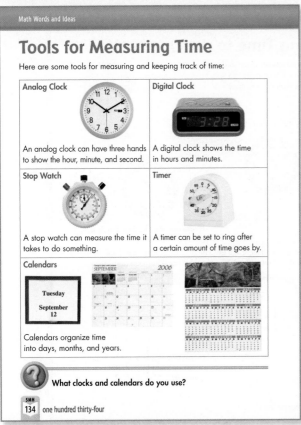

Analog Clock	Digital Clock
An analog clock can have three hands to show the hour, minute, and second.	A digital clock shows the time in hours and minutes.
Stop Watch	Timer
A stop watch can measure the time it takes to do something.	A timer can be set to ring after a certain amount of time goes by.
Calendars	

Calendars organize time into days, months, and years.

What clocks and calendars do you use?

SMH 134 one hundred thirty-four

◀ Math Words and Ideas, p. 134

Minutes in an Hour

Math Words
· minute hand

On a clock, the big hand moves every minute. It is also called the minute hand.

There are 60 minutes in one hour.

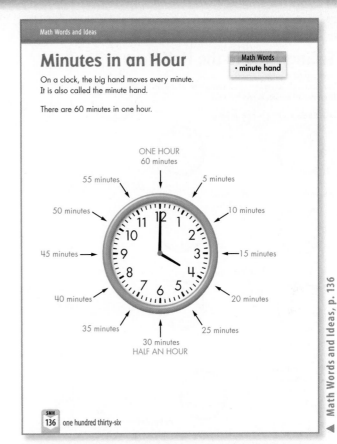

ONE HOUR
60 minutes

55 minutes · 5 minutes
50 minutes · 10 minutes
45 minutes · 15 minutes
40 minutes · 20 minutes
35 minutes · 25 minutes
30 minutes
HALF AN HOUR

SMH 136 one hundred thirty-six

◀ Math Words and Ideas, p. 136

Parts of an Hour (page 1 of 2)

Math Words
· half-hour
· half an hour

There are 60 minutes in one hour.
From 2:00 to 3:00 is one hour or 60 minutes.

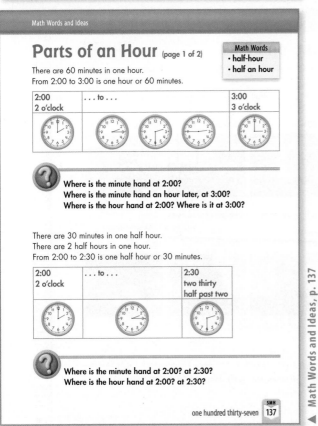

2:00 2 o'clock	. . . to . . .			3:00 3 o'clock

Where is the minute hand at 2:00?
Where is the minute hand an hour later, at 3:00?
Where is the hour hand at 2:00? Where is it at 3:00?

There are 30 minutes in one half hour.
There are 2 half hours in one hour.
From 2:00 to 2:30 is one half hour or 30 minutes.

2:00 2 o'clock	. . . to . . .	2:30 two thirty half past two

Where is the minute hand at 2:00? at 2:30?
Where is the hour hand at 2:00? at 2:30?

one hundred thirty-seven **SMH 137**

◀ Math Words and Ideas, p. 137

Parts of an Hour (page 2 of 2)

Math Words
· quarter hour

There are 15 minutes in one quarter hour.
There are 4 quarter hours in one hour.
From 2:00 to 2:15 is a quarter hour or 15 minutes.

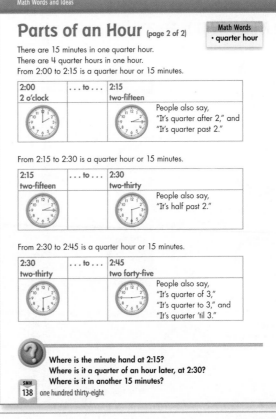

2:00 2 o'clock	. . . to . . .	2:15 two-fifteen	
			People also say, "It's quarter after 2," and "It's quarter past 2."

From 2:15 to 2:30 is a quarter hour or 15 minutes.

2:15 two-fifteen	. . . to . . .	2:30 two-thirty	
			People also say, "It's half past 2."

From 2:30 to 2:45 is a quarter hour or 15 minutes.

2:30 two-thirty	. . . to . . .	2:45 two forty-five	
			People also say, "It's quarter of 3," "It's quarter to 3," and "It's quarter 'til 3."

Where is the minute hand at 2:15?
Where is it a quarter of an hour later, at 2:30?
Where is it in another 15 minutes?

SMH 138 one hundred thirty-eight

◀ Math Words and Ideas, p. 138

Math Words and Ideas

Telling Time to the Half Hour

There are 60 minutes in an hour.
You can break 60 minutes into 2 sections of 30 minutes.
There are 30 minutes in one half hour.

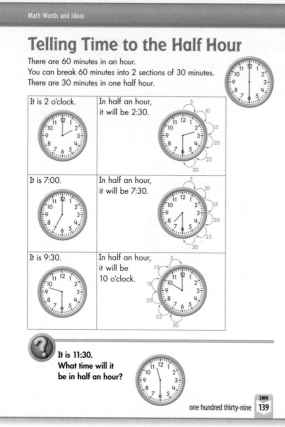

It is 2 o'clock.	In half an hour, it will be 2:30.
It is 7:00.	In half an hour, it will be 7:30.
It is 9:30.	In half an hour, it will be 10 o'clock.

? It is 11:30. What time will it be in half an hour?

◄ Math Words and Ideas, p. 139

Math Words and Ideas

Telling Time to the Quarter Hour

There are 60 minutes in an hour.
You can break 60 minutes into 4 sections of 15 minutes.
15 minutes is one quarter hour.

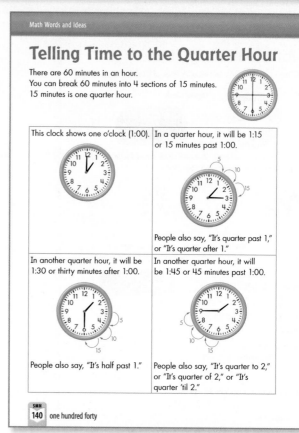

This clock shows one o'clock (1:00).	In a quarter hour, it will be 1:15 or 15 minutes past 1:00. People also say, "It's quarter past 1," or "It's quarter after 1."
In another quarter hour, it will be 1:30 or thirty minutes after 1:00. People also say, "It's half past 1."	In another quarter hour, it will be 1:45 or 45 minutes past 1:00. People also say, "It's quarter to 2," or "It's quarter of 2," or "It's quarter 'til 2."

◄ Math Words and Ideas, p. 140

Math Words and Ideas

What Time Will It Be?

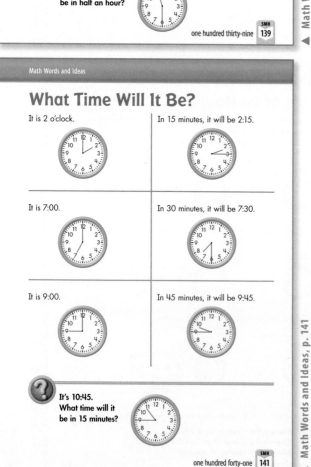

It is 2 o'clock.	In 15 minutes, it will be 2:15.
It is 7:00.	In 30 minutes, it will be 7:30.
It is 9:00.	In 45 minutes, it will be 9:45.

? It's 10:45. What time will it be in 15 minutes?

◄ Math Words and Ideas, p. 141

Math Words and Ideas

A.M. and P.M.

Math Words
• A.M.
• P.M.

There are 24 hours in one day. 12 hours are A.M. hours, and 12 hours are P.M. hours.

Times between midnight and noon are A.M. times.

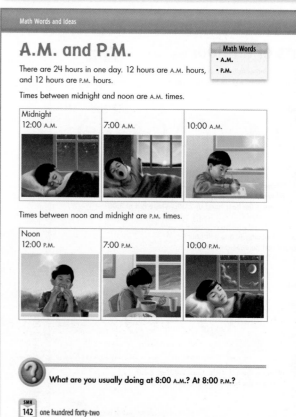

Midnight 12:00 A.M.	7:00 A.M.	10:00 A.M.

Times between noon and midnight are P.M. times.

Noon 12:00 P.M.	7:00 P.M.	10:00 P.M.

? What are you usually doing at 8:00 A.M.? At 8:00 P.M.?

◄ Math Words and Ideas, p. 142

Timelines

Timelines are another way to represent time.
Different timelines can use different units of time.

This timeline shows hours and half hours.

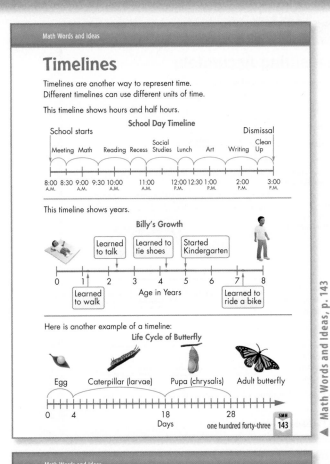

School Day Timeline

School starts — Meeting, Math, Reading, Recess, Social Studies, Lunch, Art, Writing, Clean Up — Dismissal

8:00 A.M. 8:30 A.M. 9:00 A.M. 9:30 A.M. 10:00 A.M. 11:00 A.M. 12:00 P.M. 12:30 P.M. 1:00 P.M. 2:00 P.M. 3:00 P.M.

This timeline shows years.

Billy's Growth

Learned to talk • Learned to tie shoes • Started Kindergarten

0 1 2 3 4 5 6 7 8

Learned to walk • Age in Years • Learned to ride a bike

Here is another example of a timeline:

Life Cycle of Butterfly

Egg — Caterpillar (larvae) — Pupa (chrysalis) — Adult butterfly

0   4   18   28
Days

SMH 143 one hundred forty-three

Representing Time

Schedules and timelines represent time.

Tuesday Schedule

| Morning meeting
8:00 A.M. – 9:00 A.M. |
| Math
9:00 A.M. – 10:00 A.M. |
| Writing
10:00 A.M. – 11:00 A.M. |
| Reading
11:00 A.M. – 12:00 P.M. |
| Lunch/Recess
12:00 P.M. – 1:00 P.M. |
| Science
1:00 P.M. – 2:00 P.M. |
| Clean up
2:00 P.M. – 2:30 P.M. |

Here is my schedule for one day in school.

This same day can also be shown on a timeline:

Tuesday Schedule

School starts — Morning meeting, Math, Writing, Reading, Lunch/Recess, Science, Clean up — Dismissal

8:00 A.M. 9:00 A.M. 10:00 A.M. 11:00 A.M. 12:00 P.M. 1:00 P.M. 2:00 P.M. 2:30 P.M. 3:00 P.M.

? What time does the school day begin? What time does it end? How long is this school day?

SMH 144 one hundred forty-four

Duration

Duration is the amount of time that one event lasts from beginning to end. Looking at timelines and schedules can help us think about duration.

Math class

8:00 A.M. 9:00 A.M. 10:00 A.M. 11:00 A.M. 12:00 NOON 1:00 P.M. 2:00 P.M. 3:00 P.M.

? If math class starts at 9:00 A.M. and ends at 10:00 A.M., how long is math class?

If you know the start time and the duration of an activity, you can figure out the end time.

After-school program

3:00 P.M. 4:00 P.M. 5:00 P.M. 6:00 P.M. 7:00 P.M. 8:00 P.M. 9:00 P.M.

? An after-school program starts at 3:00 and lasts $2\frac{1}{2}$ hours. When does the program end?

If you know duration and end time, you can figure out start time.

? Sally eats dinner for half an hour. She finishes dinner at 7:00 P.M. What time did she start dinner?

one hundred forty-five **SMH 145**

Measuring Length

When you measure length you measure the distance from one point to another. You can measure:

Math Words
• length
• distance
• height
• width

How far

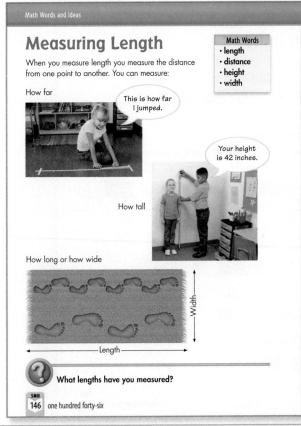

This is how far I jumped.

Your height is 42 inches.

How tall

How long or how wide

Width

Length

? What lengths have you measured?

SMH 146 one hundred forty-six

Measuring with Units

Math Words
• unit

You can use cubes to measure length. For example:

Carla can line up several cubes along the edge of the book and count the total to find the length.

This book is 11 cubes long.

She can also use one cube and repeat it, counting as she goes.

This book is 11 cubes long.

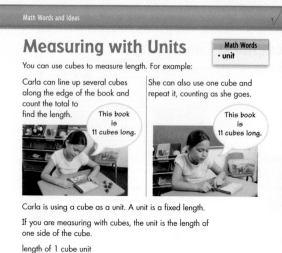

Carla is using a cube as a unit. A unit is a fixed length.

If you are measuring with cubes, the unit is the length of one side of the cube.

length of 1 cube unit

To measure accurately, all of the units must be the same size.

You cannot measure a length with these pencils because the pencils are not the same size.

The count is different because the pencils are all different sizes.

SMH
one hundred forty-seven **147**

◀ Math Words and Ideas, p. 147

Measuring Accurately

You can use units to measure the length of an object.

Length of 3 paper clips

1 2 3 4 5

Travis used paper clips to measure this pencil. He said it was 5 paper clips long.

Nate said it was 11 paper clips long. What happened?

"The paper clips aren't lined up straight."

Rochelle said it was 4 paper clips long. What happened?

"She left gaps in between the paper clips."

Anita said it was 9 paper clips long. What happened?

"The paper clips overlap each other. They should be end to end."

SMH
148 one hundred forty-eight

◀ Math Words and Ideas, p. 148

Half Units

This pencil is 16 cube units long.

If a measurement ends in the middle of a unit, you count half a unit at the end.

This pencil is $6\frac{1}{2}$ cubes long.	This pencil is $9\frac{1}{2}$ cubes long.
1 2 3 4 5 6 $\frac{1}{2}$	1 2 3 4 5 6 7 8 9 $\frac{1}{2}$

How long are these pencils?

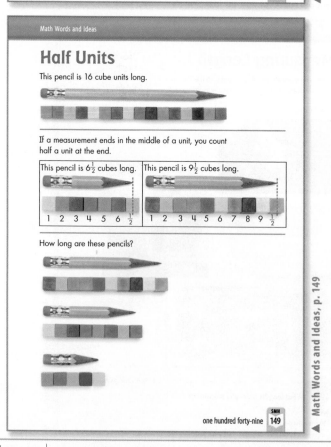

one hundred forty-nine **SMH** **149**

◀ Math Words and Ideas, p. 149

Measuring with Units of Different Lengths (page 1 of 2)

■ a cube unit   ⬭ a paper clip unit

The pencil is $16\frac{1}{2}$ cubes long.
The pencil is $5\frac{1}{2}$ paper clips long.

When you measure, the total number of units varies with the size of the unit. A bigger unit repeats fewer times. A small unit repeats more times. In other words:

• The bigger the unit, the smaller the count
• The smaller the unit, the bigger the count

? The same number of different-sized units gives different lengths. 4 cubes measure a shorter length than 4 paper clips.

Can you explain why?

SMH **150** one hundred fifty

◀ Math Words and Ideas, p. 150

Measuring with Units of Different Lengths (page 2 of 2)

If you know the relationship between the units, you can use one measurement to figure out the other.

For example, 1 paper clip is the same length as 3 cubes.

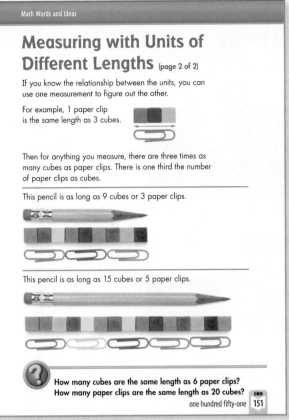

Then for anything you measure, there are three times as many cubes as paper clips. There is one third the number of paper clips as cubes.

This pencil is as long as 9 cubes or 3 paper clips.

This pencil is as long as 15 cubes or 5 paper clips.

? How many cubes are the same length as 6 paper clips? How many paper clips are the same length as 20 cubes?

one hundred fifty-one **SMH 151**

Using a Common Unit

When people need to agree on lengths and measurements, it is important that they use a common unit of measurement.

Imagine what would happen if everyone measured with units of different lengths:

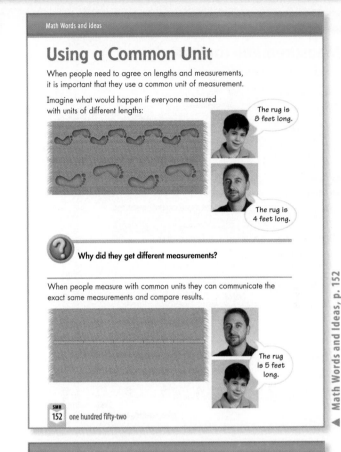

The rug is 8 feet long.

The rug is 4 feet long.

? Why did they get different measurements?

When people measure with common units they can communicate the exact same measurements and compare results.

The rug is 5 feet long.

SMH 152 one hundred fifty-two

Standard Measurement

> **Math Words**
> - inch
> - foot
> - yard

People in the United States use inches, feet, and yards to measure most distances. Only two other countries in the whole world use inches, feet, and yards. Here are some things that are *about* the same length as those measurements.

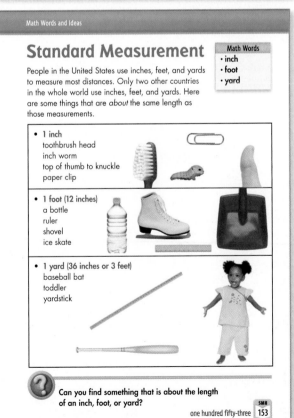

- 1 inch
  toothbrush head
  inch worm
  top of thumb to knuckle
  paper clip

- 1 foot (12 inches)
  a bottle
  ruler
  shovel
  ice skate

- 1 yard (36 inches or 3 feet)
  baseball bat
  toddler
  yardstick

? Can you find something that is about the length of an inch, foot, or yard?

one hundred fifty-three **SMH 153**

Metric System

> **Math Words**
> - Metric System
> - centimeter
> - meter

People from most other countries around the world have a different system for measuring. It is called the Metric System, and it uses centimeters and meters.

A centimeter is smaller than an inch. It takes about $2\frac{1}{2}$ centimeters to make an inch.

A meter is 100 centimeters. It is a little longer than a yard. A meter stick is useful for measuring longer objects or distances. Here are some things that are about the same length as those measurements.

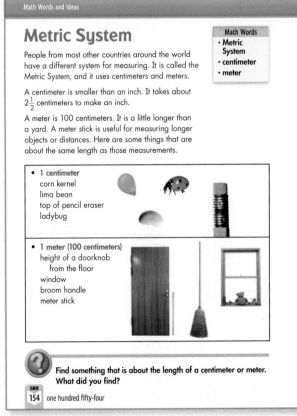

- 1 centimeter
  corn kernel
  lima bean
  top of pencil eraser
  ladybug

- 1 meter (100 centimeters)
  height of a doorknob
    from the floor
  window
  broom handle
  meter stick

? Find something that is about the length of a centimeter or meter. What did you find?

SMH 154 one hundred fifty-four

Measurement Tools: Rulers

A ruler is a tool to measure length.

This ruler measures inches.

This ruler measures centimeters.

A ruler is 12 inches (or 1 foot) long. It is about $30\frac{1}{2}$ centimeters long.

This ruler shows inches and centimeters.

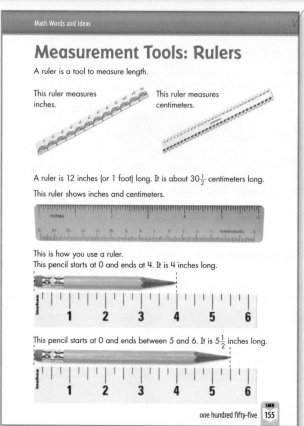

This is how you use a ruler.
This pencil starts at 0 and ends at 4. It is 4 inches long.

This pencil starts at 0 and ends between 5 and 6. It is $5\frac{1}{2}$ inches long.

one hundred fifty-five **155**

Math Words and Ideas, p. 155

Using Rulers

A ruler can be used to measure more than 12 inches or 1 foot. Start at the beginning and mark where the ruler ends. Then reposition the ruler so that it starts at your mark.

Holly uses a ruler to measure her jump.

Holly jumped 3 feet.

Darren uses a ruler to measure his jump.

I jumped $2\frac{1}{2}$ feet.

How far can you jump?

156 one hundred fifty-six

Math Words and Ideas, p. 156

Index